Marketing the Mountain

by Les Kletke

Give a man a fish, you feed him for a day. Teach a man to fish, you feed him for a lifetime. Help a man market his fish and you give him a future.

Acknowledgment

I would like to acknowledge the people at International Development Enterprises (IDE) Canada who provided me with the opportunity to see the work they are doing in Nepal and in no way steered or censored my visit.

Thank you for the opportunity to see the work that is going on, and the freedom to ask the questions I wanted to.

ISBN 978-0-9737684-5-9

All photos by Les Kletke unless otherwise credited
Les Kletke photos shot with a Cannon Eos Rebel

For copies of this book contact
Les Kletke
Box 1607
Altona, MB
Canada

lkletke@mts.net
www.leskletke.com

Printed in Canada

Dedication

For Surendra who was so much more than a translator. He became a guide to his country and culture, and he remains a treasured friend.

About IDE

IDE is a non-profit organization dedicated to increasing the income of families living on less than a dollar a day.

Since its beginning in 1981, IDE has helped to increase production and income in Africa and Asia by designing and marketing extremely low-cost products such as pedal pumps, irrigation kits, and water purifiers. IDE also develops markets that provide better opportunities for poor people.

IDE's international network has offices in Bangladesh, Cambodia, Myanmar (Burma), Nepal, Vietnam, Ethiopia, Zambia, Zimbabwe, India, Canada, UK, and USA.

For more information or to make a donation, contact:

IDE Canada
830 King Edward St
Winnipeg, MB
Canada R3H 0P5
+1-204-786-1490
info@ide-canada.org
www.ide-canada.org

IDE UK
7a The Mews
46-52 Church Road
London
UK SW13 0DQ
+44-208-288-7702
info@ide-uk.org
www.ide-uk.org

IDE USA
10403 W. Colfax Ave., #500
Lakewood, CO 80215 USA
+1-303-232-4336
info@ideorg.org
www.ide-international.org

Table of Contents

1	Welcome to Kathmandu	9
2	Cricket Dance	17
3	Tamil	27
4	Distillation Unit	35
5	Chicken Producer	43
6	Agro Vet	51
7	Lemon Grass	57
8	Engineering Shop	65
9	The Dealer	73
10	The Marketplace	81
11	The Coffee Nursery	89
12	Women Vegetable Growers	95
13	Chili Producer	103
14	Pokhara	111
15	Patan Durbar Square	121
16	Harie	131
17	Drip Irrigation	137
18	CCO Visa	143
19	Bhaktapur	151
20	Wild Earth	161
21	Saturday	169
22	Heading Home	175
23	Bangkok	183

The streets of Kathmandu offer an eclectic collection of characters.

Chapter 1
Welcome to Kathmandu

"Y ou need to pay in American dollars," said the immigration official. I had no plans to immigrate, especially to a country that did not accept its own currency as payment for a visa, but it was an indication of things to come in Nepal. The instructions I had were that a Nepalese visa costs 30 dollars American. I wrongfully assumed that they would also take the equivalent in their own currency, Nepalese rupees. I did however have my two extra passport photos ready for the visa purchase. As my instructions said, they were required.

As I neared the immigration official's desk at the Kathmandu Airport, I heard the official tell a person two or three ahead of me that they had to pay in American dollars. I was not sure about the two or three because the concept of queuing in an orderly line has not yet hit Nepal or any of Asia as far as I can tell.

Hearing the directive, I turned and headed back to the currency exchange desk that was located before the immigration desk. This should not have been too much of a problem. I would use my bank card or credit card to get some American greenbacks and some rupees and we would be set to go.

"Sorry, we don't take plastic. Do you have any other currency?" said the smiling young man behind the desk at the currency exchange. I had eliminated the Thai bhats from my wallet the night before and all I had in my wallet was a few thousand Myanmar kyats. When the largest bill is a thousand kyat denomination and worth about 80 cents US, you tend to carry about an inch of them with you, and that was all that was left.

"You will have to go downstairs to the ATM and get some rupees then come back and exchange them for dollars to buy your visa.

"The ATM?" I asked.

"It is downstairs and outside, but a lot of times it does not work, and then you will have to go into town to get some money. We do not advance any money on cards."

This was going to be more of a challenge than I thought. I decided my best chance was to get back in line and wait for the directive from the official that I need greenbacks. Then at least he would understand why I was circumventing the desks and heading downstairs. I had already noticed that there were too many armed uniformed fellows standing around for me to try and bend the rules.

So back in line I went, alternatively waiting and pushing my way to the front and got the expected response.

"You need to pay in American dollars," said the official. I played the game and explained I was aware of that but did not have any money. He said I would have to go to the ATM, and pointed down the stairs. The entire exercise was plainly a cash grab for people entering the country. It had nothing to do with security. I walked out of the arrivals part of the airport, was inundated by cab drivers trying to seduce a fare, and headed off to the ATM. I scanned the crowd for someone holding a sign with my name. No luck.

Wading through a crowd that made Christmas shopping on December 22 look like a solitary activity, I made my way back into the terminal, found the bank machine and in what appeared to be a change of luck, was about to secure some rupees on my bank card.

Dealing with another new currency, I chose to withdraw

3000 rupees because I figured that to be worth about a hundred Canadian dollars, and a good start. It worked and now I was about to do my best impersonation of a salmon going home to mate, making my way against the stream.

First obstacle, the cabbies. Since I was coming from behind them, I passed through with little problem. Next, the security checkpoint for people exiting the airport. It was more of a challenge, and some guy with a gun yelled at me to stop. I did. A brief explanation was enough, and I was on my way up the non operational escalator. It is not only the guards that don't work in this country, even the machines are a little relaxed.

I went the wrong way through the crowd emerging with their visas, over to the currency exchange to get some Yankee dollars — easy enough — and then back into the line for my third try. I decided to circumvent the line and walked up behind the desk. Thirty dollars American was the ticket for express service and I got my visa in my passport and out I went, a legal entry to Nepal. I claimed my two bags with no trouble and headed out into the bright sunshine to meet someone from IDE (International Development Enterprises).

I was confident they would have someone to meet me. They had come through on all other parts of the trip. I had already spent nearly two weeks in Thailand and Myanmar so I was comfortable with trusting them.

No luck. I scanned the crowd, and battled off a few more cab drivers before finding a place on the curb where I could check my travel documents and see if I had a contact phone number. One more cabbie came to accost me and I assured him I was alright. Business is more aggressive in Nepal than I had expected, at least business on the street.

I had no documents with any kind of number so I decided to scan the crowds on the other side of the street. These people were not allowed any closer to the terminal, for a reason I could not figure out. But then there it was, a sign with the magic words, Les Kletke.

"Why did you not come over the first time you came

out?" asked Surendra who would be my lifeline for the next two weeks.

"I had to get some money, because your country does not accept your currency." I explained.

"Say no more," he said laughing, "our car is this way. We will go to the office and meet the staff, get you something to eat, and check you into your hotel."

I liked him already and first impressions would not prove to be wrong.

The staff at the IDE Winrock offices proved to be a pleasant surprise. Their command of the English language was better than that of my son's college friends, and he goes to school in Iowa. As I learned later, Surendra had attended college in Kansas and Chicago.

IDE Country Director Bill Collis first came to Nepal with the Peace Corps in the 1970's, and had recently moved into the role of director. He had a solid understanding of the country and the goings on.

The initial meeting was one of those where they can all remember you because you are the new guy. I could not possibly keep the people, their names and duties clear in my mind. I was meeting five of them at once. I had left my hotel in Bangkok at 5 a.m. that morning and spent as much time as I could on the plane reading my travel book of Nepal. After a long day of travel, my mind was spinning just a little too fast to remember all their names in a once over.

Bill did outline that the IDE intent in Nepal was to move farmers further along the value chain. The country's agriculture was well past the subsistence stage, and IDE and Winrock were working to help farmers add value to their products and take away a bigger portion of the consumer's food dollar. I understood the concept. It was the same message that North American farmers are getting. I was about to learn how it worked on small scale agriculture.

"We are working with coffee producers, and introducing that crop," Bill said, "We think there is real potential there and we can help farmers capitalize on the image of Nepal by

Who is Jaun Valdez?

In the late 1950's the National Federation of Coffee Growers of Columbia selected a New York ad agency to launch a campaign for Columbian Coffee.

They created the fictitious Juan Valdez to personify the more than 560,000 hardworking and dedicated Columbian coffee farmers. The first Juan Valdez was a New York actor but sine 1969 he has been Carlos Sanchez of Medellin, Columbia. Sanchez is himself a coffee grower and a truly international symbol. He has been around the world marketing Columbia's coffee and has appeared at events like the US Open and Alpine Ski World Cup Finals where he supplies the spectators with free 100% Columbian Coffee throughout the events.

selling a high value coffee to Europe and the US."

"You want to be the next Jaun Valdez." I said making reference to a TV commercial from the 1970's when a New York ad agency created a character that was the typical Columbian coffee farmer bringing his crop down from the mountain in sacks on a burrow.

"Exactly" said Bill. "We want to make Nepalese coffee the symbol of quality and we think it is a good fit because of the natural organic production here. It is what the consumer of today wants."

We continued on about some of the other products that the organizations were involved in, like small scale distillation units that allowed villagers to harvest non traditional forest products and sell the oils into a waiting world market.

It was Friday afternoon, and in most offices of the country that meant knocking off early. So we decided to call it a day, and I assured Surendra I could walk back to the hotel. He pointed me in the direction of a book store where I could find some post cards and stamps. I wanted to post something home from Nepal as soon as possible.

I wandered down the street and found the bookstore that was everything he promised and more. It offered a selection of post cards that showed the beauty of the country and the faces of its people. The store also had a selection of fine rice papers and calendars, and it actually sold books along with coffee at the back of the store.

I found my way back to the hotel after a few wrong twists and turns, but no damage was done and I stored my gear in my room and proceed to the internet café that offered two computers. Both had keyboards at a most awkward height, enough to break a wrist or provide enough pain after 10 minutes that you decided to move on.

I was sitting at the computer composing a note home, when a motherly lady poked her head in the office and invited me to the wedding that was going on.

The staff at IDE had joked about me crashing the wedding and I had not taken them seriously for a second, but now this lady was inviting me. I explained that I was not part of the wedding and not properly dressed. She insisted that I needed something to eat. I considered for another 15 seconds and headed off to the buffet.

I ran into a bit of a language barrier with the other 800 guests attending the event, so I went upstairs, got my camera and did my best impression of a wedding photographer. Everyone, including the bride, was most co-operative and I spent an hour or so taking pictures of people attending the wedding before heading off to the lounge of the hotel to sample the malted beverage of Nepal. I was the only one in the bar and the bartender was more than happy to have a customer and some conversation. He explained that the wedding had started at 9:00 that morning and through the course of the day, there had been about 1,100 people in attendance. There were only about 700 at this time. He said it would be over by 9 p.m. Right on schedule the guests vacated the hotel at 9 p.m. and only a few stragglers were left by 9:30.

The manager came into the lounge and offered to be my guide the following day, since it was his day off.

"I do not want to be paid," he said, "I am offering to show you around the city. What would you like to see?"

I told him that I was not yet up to speed on the highlights of the city and would take his suggestion.

We agreed to meet in Tamil the next afternoon. That would give me some time to see the city on my own and yet have a guide for supper or any evening activities he would recommend.

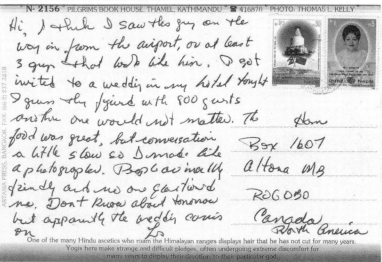

N-2156 PILGRIMS BOOK HOUSE, THAMEL, KATHMANDU ☎ 416870 PHOTO: THOMAS L. KELLY

Hi, I think I saw this guy on the way in from the airport, or at least 3 guys that look like him. I got invited to a wedding in my hotel tonight. I guess they figured with 800 guests one more would not matter. The food was great, but conversation a little slow so I made like a photographer. Basically mainly friendly and no one questioned me. Don't know about tomorrow but apparently the wedding carries on.

Ham
Box 1607
Altona MB
ROG OBO
Canada
North America

One of the many Hindu ascetics who roam the Himalayan ranges displays hair that he has not cut for many years. Yogis here make strange and difficult pledges, often undergoing extreme discomfort for many years to display their devotion to their particular god.

Maintaining traditions is still an important part of the Nepalese way of life

Chapter 2
Cricket Dance

Saturday morning. Judging from the schedule that the folks at IDE gave me the day before, I had best use the day to do some touristy things, because the rest of the time was scheduled with visits to their projects, and interviews with people involved in their work.

I went to have breakfast poolside. It wasn't until the second pot of coffee that the headache began to subside. Nothing on the breakfast buffet looked very appetizing. The eggs appeared to have a more than adequate coating of oil and while I do not consider myself a health nut, I am sure that the no-trans-fat trend had yet to hit this country. I had some yogurt and muesli with another cup of coffee and studied my travel book. It seemed that the Hotel Greenwich Village was in an ideal location and many of the major tourist attractions were within walking distance.

I could not help but notice that the fellow at the next table had a massive text book entitled "Diseases of Poultry," on the chair beside him. That did not make the eggs any more appealing so I decided to head out and see the city. I asked for a city map at the front desk. Of course they had one, it cost a buck, and I thought it was well worth the investment.

The friendly lady at the desk offered to help with directions to the tourist spots. I thanked her and explained my intention was to get some pictures of the real city and I would do that by walking towards anything that caught my attention. She smiled, shrugged and wished me a good day. I headed out armed with my newly purchased map and my camera.

After a block or two I decided it was time to ask for directions. I thought my best bet on English would be someone younger. I asked a young lady about directions to the local marketplace.

"I am heading that way to pick up a few things," she said. "You can walk with me."

I thanked her and fell into step.

"Are you a journalist?" she asked. I wondered if someone had stuck a sign on my back at breakfast.

"Yes, how did you know?"

"Your camera and you asked for a local market?" she said smiling that confident smile of someone who is comfortable having the upper hand. "Everyone else wants to go to this temple or that market. You asked for local."

She was very bright, and I asked if she was busy or if she would like to be a guide for the morning.

"I would love to be a guide, but I write my final exam tomorrow morning and I must study," she said. She was writing her final exam in electronic engineering. I had guessed her to be finishing high school. Good thing I didn't ask what she was going to do after graduation.

She led me to a marketplace that was much less formal than anything I expected, but exactly what I was looking for.

It was a collection of stalls along both sides of a street that ran parallel to what was once a river. Now it was little more than a creek with garbage lining both sides of what could have been a beautiful shoreline.

"It is a shame," she said as we walked down the incline to the street that served as a shopping center for the people of the area. We passed a pump where women were doing laundry while young boys in their underwear alternated between washing and water fighting, seeming to enjoy both equally.

The faces in the market were not those of people waiting

for some easy money from a tourist. They were the weathered faces of women who had grown the vegetables they had on the blanket in front of them.

In another booth a woman with a feather duster shooed flies from the open meat that lay on a wooden counter, which consisted of a couple of planks on two plastic pails.

My young guide seemed a little embarrassed at the market she had brought me to, but happy that she had met my request for a local market. She had indeed done that. She excused herself saying she needed to get a few things and get back to studying. I wished her well on the next day's final. She turned and disappeared while I took another picture of a vendor with mahogany colored skin arranging her vegetables.

Satisfied that I had seen some of the local market, and knowing that I would not be buying any produce, I headed across the bridge over what at one time must have been the jewel of Kathmandu. Now it was not a pleasant sight and the smell was offensive to even the strongest stomach. I wandered along the street and soon came to a temple with a courtyard that was about 6 feet below grade. It was surrounded by a 3 ft. high fence and the gate was open.

I decided to look in before entering and saw a single pump in one corner and a couple of women bathing or showering, or whatever they call the process in Nepal. It would not qualify for either in Canada. The women were at the pump and washing themselves while still wearing their sarongs. When the washing was complete, they put the dry one on over the top and removed the wet one from underneath. It was a process that allowed for a bath in public and was the most these people had ever known. It was all done quite tastefully and obviously something they had grown up with and taken for granted.

While it was quite discreet, I am sure they did not consider it a spectator sport so I moved on. I could not help thinking how good a warm shower felt and the idea of having enough water pressure to actually turn back on the tap just a bit. What I was imagining was totally different than what these women were doing in bone chilling cold water in the corner of a temple courtyard.

Continuing along the street I came to a Chinese market. I thought it would be interesting so I turned in. I walked down a lane to a three story mall of small shops offering every conceivable kitchen gadget and knock-off of brand name clothing I could imagine. There was nothing that would have me reaching into my wallet, but the trip did yield a view of a construction site where women were mixing cement by hand in what appeared to be oversize woks, then carrying them on their heads to the wall where the mason was bricking up the side of a new building. I assumed there were no

building codes in Kathmandu, or at least the inspector was not working on Saturday, because I don't think the cement would have passed the quality test for most jobs on the North American continent.

The walk lacked direction, but showed me a city that was in a hurry to get somewhere. The traffic was beyond belief and everyone seemed in that hurry up and wait mode that describes traffic jams everywhere.

It was not long until I came to a crosswalk built above the street. I thought it was a great safety advantage and made my way to the top to get some pictures of the parking lot that was the street I had been walking along. From the top of the crosswalk I saw what looked like a park with more than a dozen cricket matches underway.

I have never been a fan of a game where I don't know

who is winning even when I hear the score. I believe that sporting events, like auction sales, should end on the same day they begin, but cricket doesn't fall into that category. Nonetheless, I headed over and soon was in the middle of a few games. Before I knew it I was engaged in polite conversation with one of the fielders. He would have been in foul territory in left field on a baseball diamond. I assumed this is the place reserved for someone you do not want to handle the ball ever, and the fellow had lots of time to chat.

It did have some resemblance to baseball in the old days because of the cows grazing in the back of the field. But cows have the right of way through this country so it was not a flashback at all.

Content with having taken some pictures of the cricketers in action, I moved around to the front of the park where there were a half-dozen tents sent up. Food vendors were setting up their wares and chairs.

I was walking through the area when I met someone

acting as the marketing manager for the event that was coming up. He smiled a welcoming smile and recognized the opportunity of the camera.

"Will you stay for the dance?" he asked. I admitted my ignorance.

"The largest and longest folk dance in the world will be here this afternoon," he said knowing he had placed the hook firmly in the soft, fleshy part of my cheek. I felt like a pike about to be reeled in. Marketing people are the same the world over. They love to have the biggest and best of anything at all, but this sounded like a real deal. Judging from his costume, it would be worth the price of admission at any cost, but this was free.

He told me that the event would feature the local costumes and dances of the people of the mountains around

the Kathmandu Valley and would be starting in about an hour. I was hooked. I looked for a tent that offered some shade and sustenance.

It was not long before I found relief from the midday sun and was sitting in a plastic lawn chair surrounded by people in traditional costumes, except for one young lady. Bidisha smiled the smile of someone who knows you are lost but too proud to admit it. I asked if she spoke English.

"Of course," she said. "How can I help?"

"What is going on here?"

She explained the event in somewhat less grandiose terms than the fellow who had assumed the role of marketing manger, but it sounded worth staying at any rate. I offered to buy her a drink since I needed one and I hoped it would encourage further explanation of the event. It brought more than that.

We had barely opened our Cokes and I had just started my questions when a would-be artist showed up. With a few quick strokes of his pencil he developed a caricature of me. His offering was less than gallery quality but considering the subject, acceptable. I realized he was challenged in some ways and offered him a few rupees for his work. He accepted, smiled and moved on.

Bidisha explained that the event was not a competition between groups but rather a showcase of the local cultures that had developed in the mountain communities. The different rings that had been erected would feature different groups.

"You will see different costumes and kinds of dancing," she said. She seemed almost offended when I asked about any crossover from one ring to another.

"No, never," she said. "The people are very proud of their culture and would not dance in the ring of another. They would not know the steps and they would not want to leave their culture." The answer made sense and I decided to carry on my research with some of the food that was available.

It became apparent that barbecued chicken wings are a universal food at any "country fair" type of event. There were several tents offering them with a mix of barbecued vegetables. There were no cheeseburgers or fries, but the cold watermelon more than made up for it.

I spent the afternoon enjoying the dances and music of the different groups. While I may not have understood the history of how the differences came to be, it was quite obvious that Nepal does not have a homogenous population and many people are still proud of their heritage.

I tried to think of an event in Canada that would feature Highland dance on one stage, while the Ukrainian dancers performed on another and a third featured the hoop dancers of our aboriginal peoples. Not a bad idea. Now if only I could find a marketing guy.

Mt. FISHTAIL 6997m

Pokhara   Nepal

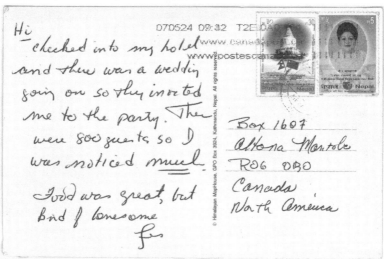

Hi
- checked into my hotel and there was a wedding going on so they invited me to the party. There were 800 guests so I was noticed much.

Food was great, but kind of lonesome

Box 1607
Altona Manitoba
R0G 0B0
Canada
North America

Everyone is open for business in Tamil, and tourists are
welcome

Chapter 3
Tamil

To the residents of Kathmandu, Tamil is not a part of the city. It is what Disneyland is to Anaheim or Disneyworld to Orlando. It is a place to work and take money from tourists who want to spend it.

It is not a place where locals go except to work. It is a separate world, as different from the rest of the city as another country might be from Nepal.

Like merchants everywhere, the sellers of any and everything can speak English. When they can't, they are able to communicate by punching their asking price on their handheld calculators, showing it to you and offering you the calculator to make a counter bid.

I stayed too long at the dance festival and had to take a cab to make my appointment with the hotel manager who would act as my guide for my visit to Tamil. I was not aware of how long a street Tamil was and expected it to be more like a square, so we had no designated meeting place. My cabbie dropped me at what he assured me was the main corner of the street.

I had barely gotten out of the car when the heavens opened, and I received another life lesson. What Canadian prairie boys think is a rain, is a light mist in other parts of the world. When it rains in Nepal at the start of the monsoon season, by comparison anything we have seen amounts to little more than a heavy fog.

I stood on the sidewalk for a while realizing that I was already drenched and could not get any wetter, when a shop keeper called me into his shop to get out of the rain. It was an easy choice, get rained on or endure another sales pitch for a carpet, which "A" I could not afford, "B" I could not take home, and "C" I did not want. I thanked him and said I preferred the rain.

"You don't have to buy anything, but come in out of the rain," he said with a welcoming smile. Did he really think I would fall for that? Soon enough I was in the shop and he offered me a stool. I found I was sharing the patch of dryness with a couple of ladies that had just come from India. Our conversation soon turned to the aggressive sales approaches of the Nepalese merchants, and in particular the merchants on this street.

"If you think this is bad, you don't want to go to India," said Madeleine who called Norway home.

"No, I find this quite relaxing after India," added Sam, a fellow traveler from the UK. The pair had teamed up in India because fair skinned young women traveling alone faced more of a challenge than they needed, so they joined forces.

We talked about our experiences in other places and the ladies shared with me some of the highlights of Tamil since they had been in town for a few days. We watched the rain come in a continuous sheet that would have washed away small animals. True to his word, the shop keeper did not even ask us if we would like to see a carpet.

The rain lasted just over an hour. It was now past 5 and I held little hope for meeting my would-be guide, primarily because of the time factor, but also because of the large crowd on the street on a Saturday night.

If anyone understands the marketing of the mountain and capitalizing on the image of Mount Everest, it is the merchants of Tamil. I did not realize there was a need for that many shops selling hiking boots, tents and trekking equipment in the whole world, much less on one street in one city.

I had no need for a North Face jacket or a sleeping bag that was good to -30, but there were more than a few merchants who were sure I did. I cannot believe that I looked like someone who was about to embark on a trek up a mountain, but that did not deter them from throwing a few pitches. I think the color of one's skin, rather than the physique, is what these fellows use when evaluating a possible customer. I was not buying. I know enough not to ask if you don't want to get involved with the bargaining system. Once you ask the price, you have indicated that you are interested and that means the hook has been placed. They will not give up, so if you don't want it, don't ask the price.

Having said that, I did fall victim to more than one street vendor and ended up bringing home a good start to the Kletke Philharmonic Orchestra.

It all started innocently enough when I stopped to listen to a fellow playing a wooden flute. I was not at all interested. I was rather tired of walking on the wet, dirty street and found his tune somewhat hypnotic. I stopped long enough to take the bait.

Before I knew it, I was in a bargaining session over a flute. He started at some ridiculous price like 20 dollars. I saw this as my out and offered him the equivalent of two, thinking he would be disgusted and tell me to get my music elsewhere. Instead he chose to get involved in the national sport of Nepal — bargaining.

This is a country that takes its bargaining seriously. Each and every transaction requires the mandatory haggle. So we were locked in mortal combat, he trying to make a living, I trying not to buy a flute I didn't need. He offered it for 18, I stayed firm at two. He explained he had come down and I had to come up. I told him I knew how the process worked but was not interested. He suddenly could not understand English and delivered another verse of the Pied Piper tune that had caught me the first time. I relented and jumped my bid to four.

He came to down to twelve and I turned and walked

away, not realizing that he was not in a stall but was free to follow me. He did and kept on for at least a block. I was approaching the next band of wandering minstrel merchants and he became desperate.

"Okay, five," he said, and threw in a story about not having eaten all day, and he was losing money, but he needed to sell something to buy food for his family.

I told him I was sorry and I did not mean to steal the flute I would rather not take it than have him lose money.

"Okay five." He insisted.

"No, I cannot take money from the mouths of your children." I said. "I cannot take it. I would never forgive myself." He saw no humor in what I thought was a good bargaining ploy.

"Five is fine."

I stuffed the flute in my bag, and he began another tune. I wonder just how low he would have gone. I know that these fellows never lose money on a deal, but imagine if they do sell one on the opening bid. It is the equivalent of winning a lottery.

I made my way to a postcard shop and found some postcards for 10 rupees each. I chose ten and asked for stamps. I wanted small denomination stamps because they had a picture of Mount Everest on them. The 30 rupee ones required for an international postcard bore only the likeness of Queen Komal Rajya Laxmi Devi Shah.

The clerk informed me that there was a 10% surcharge on stamps over what was required for the cards I bought. I agreed and told him I would use only the small domination ones and that meant 5 per card. Since I had bought 10 cards I was allowed 50 stamps. He laughed and the surcharge disappeared.

"How many do you want?" he asked. I bought a hundred, at face value. I was losing interest in what I call skin tax. Less tactfully it could be referred to as ripping off tourists. In marketing terms it could be called charging what the market would bear. Call it what you will, I was tired of it and the next guy that tried to sell me something was in for a taste of my attitude.

Along came a fiddle player and offered me a miniature violin complete with bow. I told him I had no room for the foot long weapon in my suitcase. He pulled an 8 inch version from his bag and the game was on. He started at 25 dollars. I offered him 6 and he went into the song and dance about not having sold anything today and needing food for his family.

I dropped my bid to $5.50. He explained that he would drop the price but I would have to come up. I told him I didn't want the instrument, but I wanted him to quit bothering me. He had selective hearing and offered the fiddle for 18. I walked away and he followed me for more than two blocks asking for my final offer. I told him I had already made it, and now I was done.

"Okay, okay," he said feigning the defeat of being out bargained. He said he had no change and would take the equivalent of the 6 bucks. I said I had no change and would give him 4. He said that was not fair. I agreed and said I didn't need the fiddle. He said okay and amazingly found some change in another pocket I guess he had forgotten about. I put the instrument in my bag and asked for a picture. He was happy to oblige and laughed and we shook hands. I knew full well he had bested me, but I still wondered how low he could go. It seemed a good guideline was 25% of the original asking price. That was about the bottom line, and it was where things would be sold if you stood your ground. I think

I am a thicker skinned, tougher bargainer than most, and yet I never for a moment believed that I got the better of one of these fellows who make a living performing somewhere between a salesman and an Oscar worthy actor.

By now I had wandered down to the end of a street that was dominated by butcher shops. I was surprised to find a whole wild boar on the table in some of the shops. I was shocked at the color — almost florescent pumpkin — with a small strip of bristly black hair left on the carcass. The butchers had me pegged for a question asker rather than a buyer. They refused to answer any of my queries or pose for pictures with the merchandise.

It was getting dark and I had had enough of the marketing orgy they call Tamil street, when I was surrounded by a group of rickshaw drivers. I succumbed and said I would accept a ride to my hotel in the conveyance. The driver started at some outrageous fee. We agreed on 400 rupees and I climbed aboard. We had only gone a few blocks when I asked him to take the top down. He obliged with no hesitation and folded down the top and the sheet of plastic used to make it water proof. In a few minutes were back on our way to the Hotel Greenwich. The rickshaw provided a great way to see the city as we wound down the back lanes and dueled with other rickshaws, pedestrians and bicycles. There was no possible way a car could navigate these alleys.

After a few hills where the driver was forced to get off and push the vehicle up inclines, and a half hour of travel, we were at the base of the hill that housed my hotel. The driver stopped and I feigned surprise.

"It is only a five minute walk," he said.

"It is only a five minute drive, so let's go." I said. "You were the one that asked for my business, now deliver." His English brain had gone dead, I suppose from exertion.

"I cannot," he said.

"But you asked for my business. You knew where the hotel was, and I have not gained any weight since you bothered me for the ride," I said, seeking revenge for all the pesky salesmen of the afternoon. He shrugged.

I reached into my pocket and pulled out the agreed sum.

"Twenty rupees more?" he asked.

"For what? You expect a tip for not delivering what you promised?" I asked. "You bother me for business and then don't deliver and ask for more money."

"Only twenty rupees. It is nothing for you," he said.

I gave him an extra twenty for the honesty. He admitted it was skin tax. White tourists are expected to have money falling out of their pockets and enjoy being easy marks for slick talkers. He had found his match.

I walked up the hill and turned in for the night, comfortable with my day's activities.

Hi. They do have an extensive selection of smoking material here, both equipment and smoke ables. Today some guy in Jamil wanted to sell me some hash and he could not understand that all I wanted was Coke. The real thing. I drank two before my throat noticed

Home
Box 1607
Altona Manitoba
R06 080
Canada
North America

F108. Faces of Nepal - Pondering the past over a Bidi - a cigar-like roll of tobacco.

mappost@mail.com.np

33

A small distillation unit for essential oils changes a village economy

Chapter 4
Distillation Unit

It was Sunday morning and time to get to work. The folks at IDE had scheduled a full day's activities for the day and it would be best to start with a good breakfast, so I headed downstairs to the buffet. The 6 a.m. starting time for the buffet is only a general guideline, meaning that under no conditions will items be available before that and they should be available shortly afterward.

I was enjoying my second pot of coffee when I noticed the tall gentleman who had been reading the "Diseases of Poultry" book was not reading and looked ready for a conversation. I started with the standard, "have you been here long?" Soon he invited me to join him at his table.

It turned out that John Adams was from the US and was in Nepal to present a seminar on bird flu to local producers. He was sponsored by the Winrock Foundation, which I had learned two days earlier is involved with many of the same projects as IDE and partners with them on much of the funding.

It turned out that John was waiting for his translator/guide, much as I was, and then we were off to the airport for a flight to cities neither of us could remember the name of. Our guides turned up at the same time and obviously knew each other from their work. In a matter of minutes we established that we were heading for the same plane to Nepalgunj and decided to share a cab. Four passengers would not be a load for a North American taxi, but in Nepal it was a challenge that would rate close to trying to stuff college kids into a Volkswagen Bug. We piled in, our gear safely stowed, and headed to the airport discussing the state of agriculture in Nepal.

Having just spent two weeks in Myanmar seeing agriculture at the subsistence level, I was surprised by the development of Nepalese agriculture and the advanced nature of programs IDE was implementing. The first stop was a distillation unit that processed high value oils from crops grown in community forests.

The project had begun just over a year ago and was already yielding dividends for the village. The distillation unit was built at a cost of 1 million rupees and provided direct benefit to 58 households and another 760 households that sold product to the distillation unit.

"Look at the poles," said the manager when I asked what difference the project had made to his village. "We are getting electricity. We have already put up the poles and within the year we will have power in the village." That's progress!

A tour of the village later showed me that pumps had been installed in every yard so that each house had access to water.

"We used to have three pumps for the entire village," said the manager, "one at each end and one in the middle. Now everyone has water." He was obviously proud of the impact the project was having under his management.

He had the job of managing the unit which consisted of a small boiler and a distillation unit that used a ground-fed stream as a cooling source, but he was also expanding his own production of plants. At the time he had a hectare and a half under cultivation. The crop inputs had cost him 30,000 rupees and the crop had yielded 90,000 rupees worth of valuable crop. His intention was to expand his operation to four or five hectares of chamomile and bring his production up to six kilos of oil per hectare instead of the current five.

"It is a new crop and we are still learning how to grow it," he said. "As we know more about the plant we will increase the yield." The chamomile had brought farmers in the project a return of 51,600 rupees the previous year, but this year's price had jumped the return to 220,000 rupees.

The village had the benefit of 16.4 million rupees generated by the distillation unit with another 492,000 rupees coming from custom tolling of crops for non members of the project.

The money was generated from less than 30 hectares of land: 7 hectares from the village's own community forest, 13 hectares from other community forests, and 6 hectares from private lands. Cultivated annual grasses included mentha and chamomile, while perennials included lemongrass, citronella and palmerosa. Eucalyptus, which is harvested from the wild, earned the highest returns at 195,000 rupees per kilogram.

The distillation unit is located only 150 km from the

Indian border, which has a ready market for any of the oils. They are further processed in India before being sold to China.

The distillation unit has a good "green report card" almost by accident. The spent straw of the crops that have been used for oil extraction is used as fuel for the boiler. The water that is used for cooling in the distillation chamber is then used to irrigate nearby crops.

The value of crop

produced per hectare would have many North American farmers shaking their heads and thinking that the numbers were impossible to generate.

Here was a Third World country that was doing exactly what Canadian farmers are being told to do, but have not been able to latch onto. In the most rural area of Nepal, the poorest of the poor were making the leap to harvesting products the world wants, processing them in their own village and exporting a high value product that had virtually no transportation costs. It appeared that I was in for more than one surprise on this day, and it was only mid afternoon.

It was only when I got back to the room for the night and began to do the calculations that I wondered if Canadian farmers would be able to compete in any area, or had we become too big to generate the kind of money this village was earning on a small scale? Are we ever going to be able to compete as low cost producers as new land in Eastern Europe becomes available for six dollars an acre, or as Brazil opens up its huge land mass capable of producing three crops a year.

Canadian farmers truly are between a rock and a hard place when it comes to adding value to their crops. The size of their operation and lack of market for value-added products leaves them at a distinct disadvantage. Here in the forests of Nepal it seemed easier for the farm to make the transition from little more than subsistence agriculture to producing a product that had to be stored under lock and key because of its high value and low volume.

A final chat with the manager revealed that the market was only increasing for the products that his plant was producing.

"We are currently working 250 days of the year. Our goal is to have the plant working 300 days," he said. "If I phone a buyer in India he is here the next day, and the price of oils keeps on increasing every year. Some of the oils went up by 50% this year".

While the future looked bright for the harvesting of forest products, the village was not putting all its eggs in one basket.

"We are using some of the money from the distillation unit to buy IDE pumps for irrigation of our onions, cauliflower and cabbage. More water increases the quantity and quality of the crop."

A tour of the village showed that vegetable production was being taken seriously and the local vegetable co-operative was holding a meeting. The group was making decisions about marketing the current crop and seed purchases for the next growing season. The purchase of treadle pumps meant that the group was harvesting crops — even at the end of the dry season, something that would not have happened before irrigation.

The co-operative was holding its meeting on the deck of its own building. Profits had been used to build a multipurpose building that provided office space (equipment was not yet there) and a classroom for extension meetings.

Next to the co-operative's building a young lady was herding two cows into a small pen as we arrived.

"She found them in the community forest," explained the manager of the distillation unit. "The owner will have to claim them and explain why they were loose and in the community forest where they can do damage to the valuable crops. Owners are responsible to keep their cattle at home."

She penned the two cows and headed back into the forest with her friend. I did not find out if the job of cattle jailer was a paid one or if it was just a community duty she performed after finding the two cows in the forest. Either way they were in jail until the owner came to claim them and he had best come with an explanation.

A further tour of the village revealed a brand new tractor waiting for what appeared to be its first action in the field. As I looked at the Indian-made tractor that resembled a Ford, right down to the paint color, an elderly gentleman appeared.

"He is the mayor of the village. His father started the village," said the distillation unit manager who was now acting as a city guide. I asked the senior to climb aboard for a picture. He obliged happily.

The entire village would benefit from the tractor through custom work.

"No one could afford a tractor themselves," said my guide. "He is well-to-do and bought the tractor. Now he counts on the rest of the village to help him pay for it by hiring him to till their fields." I could not help but wonder if that concept could work in North America. Not one tractor per village, but somehow reducing the capital on farms by having more than one farm use a piece of equipment. The days of agriculture providing enough income for a farm to own a full line of machinery may have gone the way of the horse and steam engine, especially if we have to compete with people from this side of the world where labor costs are not an issue.

We headed back to the car and down the trail that the villagers considered to be a road. Obviously when transportation is a bicycle or your feet, a few potholes are not a serious issue. I could only imagine what kind of a swamp the road would become in the rainy season. I would be home by then.

Hello
    Went out to the county and start the interview today. Farmers here have so little - the capital investment is a spade and if your lucky a pair of oxen. No John Deere dealers —
                    Jes

Box 1607
Altona Manitoba
R0G 0B0
Canada
North America

Raising chickens provided an opportunity for Subedi after the death of her husband

Chapter 5
Chicken Producer

The number of chickens that a large barn in North America loses in a day would provide a livelihood for Radhika Subedi.

Subedi raises 200 birds near Nepalgunj and said that since she started in the poultry business it has changed her life. Her husband died leaving her with family debt and two small children. With no economic activity to pursue, she had few choices to provide a living for her and her children.

Why did she choose the poultry business?

"It looked like people that were raising chickens were making money, so I thought it was something I could do," said the petite woman seated only a few feet from the building that houses her birds at one end and provides living space for her and her family at the other end. Two water buffalo graze contentedly in the side yard and she explains that they are both pregnant. While she had no land to use the beasts for draught, she plans to raise the calves and sell them for extra income.

Her operation appears to be thriving, with healthy birds in one end of the barn and the expectant water buffalo munching on the greenery around the house. It has not been an easy transition to agricultural producer.

"I did not know anything about chickens when I started," she admitted with a shy smile, "but I had to do something to provide a living for my family and this seemed like something

I could do." Today, two years after the start of the operation, she is much more aware of the problems of poultry production and the diseases that affect the birds.

She keeps the birds from 42 to 50 days. When they reach a weight of 4.2 pounds she sells them either to individuals who come to visit her farm at the edge of town or to larger dealers that transport them to the city where they are sold in the marketplace. When individuals come to purchase a bird, she does not let them in the flock because of the disruption, but rather asks how heavy a bird they would like and picks an appropriate one.

"I never miss," she said with a twinkle in her eye. "I don't have to go back to get a second one. I know what my birds weigh."

My mind wandered back to the broiler operations in Manitoba where production has been cut from 60 down to 38 days per cycle in just the twenty years I have been covering the industry and the size of the barns has increased as farmers amalgamate their quotas to justify having a barn manager.

The lady who had taken time to visit with me was without a doubt the best dressed poultry producer I have ever interviewed. The gold bangles jingled at her wrist as she sat comfortably on a plastic lawn chair in her front yard doing her best to answer the machine-gun-like questions I had. Time was of the essence for me, and I knew that I had to move on, but somehow I wanted to take more time to visit with this 98 pounds of determination who had developed an enterprise against long odds.

North American producers have access to the best genetics in the world, and that is why birds are now ready for market in half the time they were when I started to cover the industry. Subedi has trouble getting the chicks she wants, and is told they are not available. She knows there are better genetics available but she does not have access to them.

"The supplier does not give me quality chicks. But I cannot change suppliers because he is the one that is close by and provides delivery. I have no bargaining power to go to the supplier down the road," she said.

She knew there was a Nepalese bred bird that would give her much better returns. Not only was she at the mercy of the supplier for delivery and genetics, but his prices were outrageous by North American standards. She was forced to pay five to seven rupees a chick for the day old birds.

The irony is that good poultry genetics are available worldwide, and the companies that improve the growth rates of the birds are located anywhere and everywhere, but the Indian supplier says this is all Subedi can get.

Because of the high demand for chicks she does not have chickens of a single sex. She has poults and cocks in the same flock. It adds to her problems and the pecking of birds. "When I ask him about the availability of sexed chicks he says they are not available," she says.

I remember that being an issue on the Kletke homestead in the days when I was assigned the task of feeding the chickens that came to live there every spring and would end up in the freezer or be sold to provide a little extra cash for Mom in the fall.

Subedi is working with genetics at least that old and is making a living for her son and daughter. Her daughter is completing a degree in Arts, while her son is younger and will receive a certificate in Arts this year. All that on 200 chickens turned over 5 times a year.

The total loan for her operation when she began was 59,000 rupees. After only two years of living off the operation and paying down the family debt that was left after the death of her husband, she is down to owing 49,000 rupees on the loan.

"It will go more quickly now that I have paid off the personal debt," she said, "especially if I could get more chickens. The supplier keeps promising me more but when he delivers there are never any more in the boxes."

Her loan came from the Kdihaynagar Women Self Help group which was formed in November of 2003 by the Nirdhan Uthan Bank. It allows women like Subedi to have the dignity of earning their own living through their own business.

Subedi has plans for the future. She would like to expand her flock to 350 – 400 birds and then begin saving for her own house instead of renting the current facility which houses both her and the birds.

I can't help but compare the situation in Canada to what I have seen today. Both are chicken producers and when the final product ends up on the dinner plate, most people would be hard pressed to tell the difference.

The Canadian producer is concerned about open borders and being flooded by chickens from the United States which are grown on massive production units that work every component down to the lowest cost. On any give day a feed ration can change if barley is cheaper than corn or vice versa at the time the feed order is placed.

Canadian producers have worked under the supply management system for more than 30 years. It has provided them with a good living and has allowed for genetic improvements in the birds because of market returns.

Now fast food restaurants are putting pressure on producers to raise their birds in more humane conditions. The folks at MacDonalds or Kentucky Fried Chicken have a huge influence on the production practices of farmers.

In Nepal a widow is trying to pay off the debt of her late husband and provide an education for her children. She too must deal with the faceless large corporation, but in a very different way.

She wants access to the best genetics and the best birds available so that she can make a better living in order to pay down her debt and own a home, regardless of how humble it is by North American standards. The company that supplies her birds will not take her seriously because they know that she has no other choice of a supplier.

The scenario seems so different at first glance but both producers, Nepalese or Canadian, are feeling the pinch of the large corporation not reacting to their demands.

The practices in the barn might be a little different, but

the practices in the boardroom are much the same. The producers are the ones who take the conditions that are handed to them.

Our time was up and we had to move on. I was impressed with the entrepeneurship and the management skills this woman had developed after being thrust into the poultry business.

As we headed into the village I asked about the large clay pots that were at the entrance of every house. They were obviously storage systems of some kind.

"They are clay, and made by hand," said Surendra, "They are used for everything from lentils to grains like rice." He

goes on to explain that the opening at the bottom allows entry when the grain is below the level that can be reached from the top. The clay not only keeps moisture from the grains but also keeps it safe from any rodent that might be looking for a snack.

Walking along the village's only street we passed a butcher shop. I wondered if he was one of Subedi's customers, buying birds at the edge of town and selling them to shoppers in the village.

The shop is actually just a table beside the street with a pole that has a balance beam hanging from it. There is no refrigeration and no electronic scale as we have become accustomed to in North American shopping centers. A customer tells the butcher what kind of meat she wants and indicates the approximate amount on the carcass. The butcher proceeds to accommodate the request with a large cleaver. He then does his best to measure the amount of the purchase with a series of weights on the other side of the balance beam and the transaction is completed.

Shopping really is different in other parts of the world. There is something to be said for the freshness of the product.

Spring is the wedding season and red the traditional color of brides

Traffic on the streets of Kathmandu

Businesses of Kathmandu can not wait for construction crews

The market place in Tamil offers a full range of souvenirs and wild boar

Selling produce on the streets of Kathmandu

The moghul-inspired Krishna Mandir in Patan

Terraces on the hills of the Kathmandu Valley

Traditional costumes come alive at a dance festival

I am sure the beasts were oinking, or mooing or clucking that morning but, refrigeration would go along way to maintaining the quality of the product past the afternoon.

Ayutthaya
THAILAND

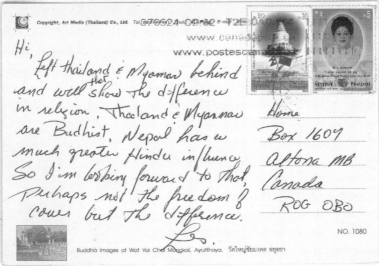

Hi,
Left thailand & Myanmar behind
and will *that show the difference
in religion. Thailand & Myanmar
are Budhist, Nepal has a
much greater Hindu influence
So I'm looking forward to that.
Perhaps not the freedom of
cows but the difference.

Home
Box 1609
Altona MB
Canada
ROG OB0

NO. 1080

Buddha images at Wat Yai Chai Mongkol, Ayutthaya. วัดใหญ่ชัยมงคล อยุธยา

49

Seeds from around the world find their way to rural Nepal

Chapter 6
Agro Vet

I t is a throw back to the days when the farm supply store had everything you could possibly need on the farm. That is missing from the modern country supply store in North America. Fifty years ago there was the pot bellied stove and a lively game of checkers in the back.

On Hung does not have time for a game of checkers. His shop may appear cluttered as a farm supply store did at one time in North America, but his business is competitive, and he has to concentrate on service and information on entrapment for his clients.

There are 11 other Agro Vet stores in the area, encompassing 90 villages and 10,000 people, and business is competitive.

"The demand for technology is increasing," said Hung. "People see that they can do better with better seeds and equipment and they want the return."

Extension of agricultural information comes in a mix of government agencies, private industry and NGO's (Non-Governmental Organizations). He says that farmers are hungry for information and want to better their lot. They do not care where the information comes from, they just want to know what will give them the best crops and the best return from the limited money they have for inputs.

Like everywhere else in the world, farmers view other farmers as the best source of information about what will work on their farm.

"If a farmer tries a new method or a new seed and it is successful, other farmers will be here for it next year," he said. "They trust what they see on their neighbor's farm, where they can watch it all the time."

He uses the example of hybrid seed.

"Farmers know that hybrid seed will provide them with a better yield, so they have made the switch, except in canning tomatoes," he said. "The local variety is better for canning and making chutney, which is a huge part of our diet, so they use the local variety for that and it brings a better return in the marketplace." It is just one of the examples of the information required in the competitive farm supply business of rural Nepal.

Hung knows that the local variety is best for canning tomatoes, but that is only one sector of the market and he carries seed from Denmark, Holland, Thailand, India and the US as well as the open pollinated varieties of seeds from his country that many farmers produce and collect themselves.

"Generally hybrid seeds produce double the yield," he said. "But in some cases, like canning, quality is the issue and farmers can make more money delivering a quality product that the housewife wants."

Hung has decided to concentrate on the information aspect to give his business an advantage over the other Agro Vet stores in the area. He tries to keep up with the latest in research and makes the translation as to what it will mean on the farms in his local area. He has purchased a photocopy machine so that he can provide farmers with information about products and practices. The machine has proven so popular that it is now a separate business operated by his wife in the next stall of the row of shops that line the main street going through the village of Kohalpur.

While we were having tea in his shop, a farmer came by to purchase three grams of carrot seed. It is a strange time of the year for carrot seed. When the transaction had been completed and he had the five rupee payment in his hand, the customer explained that he wanted the seed for a herbal medicine. Hung explained that it would be of no value and refunded the customer his money. "The hybrid seed would not work for the remedy that many hope to make," Hung said. He would not take rupees for an ineffective remedy. Recipes and home remedies are just a part of the farm supply business in Nepal.

Hung said his eight years in business have been good and have allowed him to expand his showroom to carry a broader line of products. Some of the products would be very difficult to find, even in the most well-stocked North American shop. "We have dewormer for the water buffalo. Since they

are not a commercial animal, raised for slaughter as your cattle in North America are, it is important that they be dewormed twice a year so they can stay healthy to till the fields," he says. He also carries a full line of poultry supplies and treatments. "But the size of poultry operations varies from large commercial operations to farms with two or three hens. Those birds are just as important to them and we have to service that market as well."

He says that while many of the farmers try to use 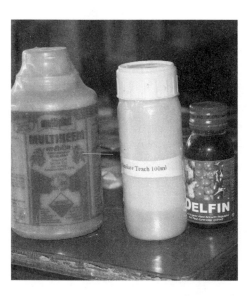 integrated pest management systems that rely on natural methods, there is still a considerable demand for pesticides. It is here that he has a great deal of trouble. "Most of our pesticides come from India where there are few regulations and little if any information, so the quality of the product varies greatly," says Hung. "We have some suppliers that are consistent with a good products, but there are others who do not care about the quality of the product and will sell us anything."

"We also have some middle men who will doctor the product. By the time it gets to the retail outlet, it has been cut several times to increase the profit and so it will be much less effective."

How does he plan to stay viable in the increasingly competitive farm supply business?

"I will keep up to date so that I can provide farmers with good information and they will come to trust me," he said . "I have to keep my price down and provide extra hours of service."

He does not complain about the conditions he faces. He maintains that the business has provided him a good living and he has plans to continue in it. He counts himself lucky to live at the back of the shop so he is available if a farmer needs something after hours. He is confident that seed companies will continue to provide better products that will be in demand by the farmers of Nepal.

Hi. Some people came for the drugs in the 70's and stayed. One of them runs a hotel where I stayed on Sunday night. She does understand food and is trying to train the staff on the service concept but nothing happens over night here. People are incredibly patient with change or anything moving forward - but they do enjoy a good trip

F7 The road to ecstasy at Pashupatinath, Kathmandu

Box 1607
Altona Manitoba
R0G 0B0
Canada
North America

Photo- Jagadish Tiwari

Lemon grass is a valuable crop that needs to be guarded from the cows

Chapter 7
Lemon Grass

I wondered why the couple was out walking in the field. They were obviously locals and I had noticed them earlier when we passed by on the road. We had to double back to gain access to the field and now they were making their way towards us.

It was a bright Sunday afternoon and a nice day for a walk, but my impression of Nepalese villagers was that they were more occupied with making a living than enjoying the sunny afternoon.

"They are guarding the field," said Surendra. "It is their turn. The villagers take turns watching the fields and chasing animals away." It was apparent that cows are the same the world over. They will eat precisely what they are not supposed to. Given the long odds of finding a patch of lemon grass among the rest of the hillside available for grazing they would find it, and they did.

It was not long before a pair of cows wandered over the hill and made their way toward the plot of lemon grass. They were not moving at breakneck speed, but their grazing certainly had direction.

The woman took the lead in making sure the cows would not do damage to the valuable crop, and sent the man to move the cows away. I cannot understand Nepalese, but the tone of her voice and the motion of her hand made me understand the message. Obviously her partner did as well because he wasted little time in getting after the cows. It was one of the few times that I saw a man move quickly in rural Nepal.

It would appear that the eating habits of cows are no better than those of humans and they don't know what is good for them. Lemongrass is unpalatable for the animals. It is considered an invasive weed in pastures. Animals will starve if it overtakes a pasture.

The grass was just one of the crops the village had under cultivation. Lemongrass, along with other crops is harvested from the community forest, then distilled at a nearby village and sold to buyers in India. The oil of lemongrass sold for 800 rupees per kilogram and brought a substantial amount of money to the local economy.

The production of essential oils has proven a boon for many rural villages. The harvesting of non-traditional forest products is a major focus of IDE and Winrock programs. Harvesting of plants that grow naturally in the forest is allowed under the Nepalese reforestation program. Harvesting means that local people pay more attention to the reforestation program because it provides them with income from the land turned back to forest.

The reforestation has coincided with a dramatic increase in the demand for essential oils worldwide. Essential oils by definition are oils that carry a distinctive scent (essence) of the plant.

Lemongrass is widely used in cooking, but the hard outside of the stalk that makes it unpalatable for animals also makes it difficult to cook with. It is only the inside that is used in cooking for most recipes.

The grass does produce citronella oil which is used in the production of insect repellent and has been proven as effective as DEET.

Our interview complete, we began the journey to our hotel, which Bill of IDE had promised me would be a treat. He was a man of his word. The hotel was a complex of three two-story guest houses each containing four rooms comfortably, though not elaborately, furnished. The shower worked and the bed was firm which was all I needed.

It was far from bedtime. Three individuals from IDE arrived shortly after we did and we gathered for a discussion in the courtyard over some cool refreshments. The talk began with an outline of projects that IDE and other developmental organizations are involved in.

Having worked as an agronomist in Russia, I had some understanding of the challenges of extension work in countries where the flow of information is not quite the same as in North America.

"The greatest challenge here is that we work to establish an enterprise, but we know that we are only going to be here a few years," said one of the visitors. "We have to provide the information and establish an enterprise and move on. Our business is development and to plant the seed."

"How do you do that while providing basic extension?" I asked.

"We work with the government, and while we provide expertise to start an enterprise we also train government workers to provide the ongoing extension work," he said. Formidable tasks indeed.

He acknowledged that there was a government extension network and in most cases the individuals were more than willing to work with organizations like IDE.

"They have no funds," he continued. "They are good people who want to help the local people, but after a while they get frustrated at having no resources and not being able to do anything. When a company comes along that can provide some help and opportunity they are very willing to work with us. The key is always to make things sustainable so that they can continue after our support ends. We can only be here for a short time."

It was not long before our talk turned to commodity prices and the future for farmers facing falling prices as they were.

One of the group had done his master's thesis on the price of vegetables at the farm gate. He told me how the price of cauliflower had dropped over the last twenty years.

"The farmer is getting less now than he was twenty years ago," he said. "There is no hope of the price returning. It just continues to go down."

I asked about increased production and how the volume of product had increased and if the introduction of new seed types and fertilizer had an impact.

"Of course, but the farmer continues to get less. He is pressured to produce more on the same amount of land because he gets a lower return from the marketplace."

I looked around to make sure I was not at a farm meeting in Western Canada. The comments were the same and it was a message I have heard all too often in twenty years of covering farm meetings. I started as a farm broadcaster about the same year this guy used as a base year for the price of cauliflower.

I shared with him that the price of wheat had been going down since the days when the Egyptians started to cultivate it and that apart from a few spikes, like during the World Wars and the 1970's, the trend line was down.

He said he had not studied the price of wheat, but accepted the information. The price lines were the same and the message to the farmer was the same. They were getting less for their products which were viewed as raw ingredients in the food chain. The only real option was to move closer to the consumer if they wanted to get a larger portion of the consumer's food dollar.

Darkness was settling in on the court yard and Surendra suggested we go for dinner. All the talk about food had served to whet my appetite and we made our way to the dining room. He ordered a traditional Nepalese meal with an appetizer that was a mix of peanuts, onions and some chili sauce. I like hot food, and normally can handle just about anything the locals will throw at me. I pride myself in being able to enjoy things about as hot as they come. I have been known to ask for a little more on items that have a three alarm heat rating, but this one stopped me. This was, bar none, the hottest thing I have ever had in my life. I loved it. Sometimes the heat is overpowering and the taste is lost. This dish still tasted great, but the heat put the brakes on the Great White Eater. I left some on the plate.

Actually we had more than enough for ourselves. I was able to share some with the lady dining alone at the next table. She was from Norway and with the UN delegation that was in the area. She had spent time with the Save the Children organization and was now part of an observation delegation evaluating conditions in rural Nepal.

Supper was excellent, and I was just about done when Linda appeared. She was the lady Bill had said made this place a must see.

Linda was a full sized woman who appeared from

the kitchen with a tie- dyed tank top, matching ¾ length pants, and a direct manner.

"I came as a hippie in the 70's and fell in love with the country. I went home to Minnesota to clean up a few things and then came to stay," she said. "That was 30 years ago and I still love this place."

"How long you been here?" she asked. I told her "a couple of weeks."

"You're tougher than most, still eating the local food," she said motioning to my plate. "Most people order a cheeseburger by their second week. I can tell how long you have been here by what you order."

She almost paused. "What do you want for breakfast?" Bill had warned me about this. You get to order at supper and you don't change your mind.

"I have maple syrup for the French toast. Only place in the country that has maple syrup," she said.

She shared a story about growing up in the northern US and going to Canada as a young girl and having real maple syrup and not liking it because she was so used to the artificial stuff.

"Of course with five kids my folks couldn't afford the real stuff, and neither can I, but this is pretty good."

I ordered the French toast and she asked me again, with a warning that there were no changes after that.

The business of food out of the way, Linda took the time to explain her view of American politics. There was little doubt that she would handle things differently than current President Bush.

Her awareness of the world situation was amazing and I asked about her ability to stay abreast of American politics in rural Nepal.

"I have a satellite dish," she explained. "I get CNN. Of course you don't in the rooms, but I do in the house."

Her direct approach was somewhat refreshing and her definite opinions on most everything were almost Texan, yet diametrically opposed to the Texan in the White House.

We shared a few more stories around the dinner table before I called it a night.

THE ANNAPURNA HIMALAYAN RANGE

POKHARA

nepal

070524 09:32 T2E

www.can

www.postesca

Hi
Stayed in a hotel that is
owned by an American that
came in the 70's and didn't
go home. I haven't seen
tye-dyed clothes for a while
but she has a set. Food
was good and I had the
hottest peanut/garlic thing
I have ever eaten. Wow
Les.

Box 1607
Altona Manitoba
R0G 0B0
Canada
North America

The Quality Control department makes a final inspection of a new pump

Chapter 8
Engineering Shop

A breakfast of French toast and maple syrup washed down with a couple of mugs of coffee, in a nice court yard goes a long way to starting the day. It helps one ignore the constant shouting coming from the training field across the street — helps, but docs not overcome it.

"That is a police academy," said Surendra in reply to my quizzical look after a particularly loud, long outburst. The noises had been coming from the neighboring field yesterday as well, but I was surprised that it began so early the next morning.

"It is training drills. They go on all the time," he said. It was time for us to move on. I was sure that my day was off to a better start than the fellows that were getting barked at across the street.

We got into our car and squeezed out of the parking space between the white four-wheel-drive SUVs that bore the UN logo. I made some comment about the number of United Nations vehicles I had seen on the trip.

"It is easy to come and evaluate human rights, when you live on the outside," said Surendra. "But human rights are not so much of an issue when you are busy making a living." My mind went back to the lady beside us at supper last night, the one from Norway. I thought about Surendra's words. Indeed it was much easier to go out and save the world when you live in one of the most socialist countries with one of the highest standards of living in the world.

Human rights and animal rights are something that people think of when all their needs are met and they need a cause to pursue. But hunger is an all-consuming passion. It determines what your actions for the day will be — trying to get enough to eat.

Working in Russia had shown me that hungry people  make poor long-term decisions. I was surprised at the lack of livestock on farms I visited there. When I asked about breeding stock and where they would get animals from once they increased their feed grain production, I was told that the breeding stock had been butchered and eaten. Being hungry does get your attention. It is something that most North Americans have never experienced. There is not much use saving the bull for next year's breeding program when you face starvation.

My travels have taught me that people want two things: a safe, warm place to live with enough to eat, and a better life for their children. The way they approach it may be different and the standards of what they expect are greatly different, but those are the basic goals of people around the world.

"What about the thousands of babies that die every year in Nepal?" asked Surendra. "Don't they have human rights?

Their right to life is taken away before it gets started." I asked about the number of deaths.

"Yes, thousands of babies die in this country because of simple things like diarrhea and other things that could easily be prevented with proper care or clean water." I thought about the fuel those SUV's were using, never mind the cost of the vehicles themselves. I wondered how many lives would be saved if that money was used to provide pre-natal classes for new mothers or clean water for their homes.

I don't doubt the good intentions of people like the woman from Norway, but does another report by another person from a well-to-do country really do anything? My observation was that the people of Nepal are well educated and have the initiative to improve their lot in life. What is missing is the capital to get started. If the money spent on observers was used to hire local people, it would go a lot further to driving economic growth and building a sustainable economy.

"Here we are," said Surendra, his voice bringing me back to reality. Developing a plan to save the world would have to wait. It was time to visit a workshop that built the IDE pumps.

Mr. Yuvak Dangi met us at the front of his shop and offered the traditional welcome. It was obvious that he was more comfortable making decisions about crunching metal than dealing with some foreign journalist with a notebook and camera.

Dangi's father started the business in 1991 to manufacture window grills and shutters for businesses. Today it employs ten people and still makes the same security products, but has included the pumps that IDE sells to farmers in its product line. He said the average employee had been with him six or seven years.

The IDE policy is that local manufacture of pumps is strongly encouraged. The income from the sale of the pumps remains in the country. The twin cylinder pump that can deliver approximately 10,000 liters of water an hour to a field, sells for less than ten dollars. That is the guideline for IDE's product line. Items have to be affordable in the local economy and in Nepal, that means under ten bucks. The pump sells for that price and allows for a profit on the sale for the distributor as well as the in-country manufacturer.

The cost of research and development of the products is borne by the parent IDE organization.

In the just under three years that Dangi has been involved with IDE through their training program, the shop has produced nearly three thousand pumps with a value of over a million rupees and a profit for his business of nearly 70,000 rupees. That is money that stayed in the local economy, and provided jobs for other people in the village.

Dangi planned to expand his business to another shop in

a village two kilometers down the road. He wants to maintain this site but feels that the other shop would increase production "and provide better market penetration". It is a strange mix of almost primitive production methods and modern day business acumen.

His terminology triggered some business questions and I asked him about the supply chain. He replied that he was happy with the distributor and dealer network that IDE had helped establish. While most dealers carried a supply of parts for the pumps, he also had a full supply of parts on hand if farmers came by to get repairs directly from him.

I asked about the supply of steel and why he chose to cut flat steel and roll and weld it into cylinders for the pumps. "Wouldn't it be easier to buy pipe, or is it not available?"

"The quality is not good. The pipe we get is too rough on the inside and would wear out the pistons of the pump, plus it is not good enough to hold the water. There are leaks in the weld of the pipe we get," he said, "so we make our own."

We walked out back to see the quality control department. Two men were testing the cylinders of a just-finished pump for leaks. The testing consisted of closing off the cylinder and while one fellow applied pressure from the top, the other delivered a visual inspection for any leaks. Since the pumps are powered by the treadle mechanism and have the capacity to pull water from about 20 feet below ground, the pressure applied was several times more than the pump would ever experience in the field. It was not what one would expect in a North American plant with some electronic gadgetry inspecting welds, but it was no less effective. Any pump that had a flaw could be sent back to the welding station that was less than a meter away. There would be little doubt about the problem if anything was returned to the welding station. It may have seemed archaic, but there was no doubting the efficiency or effectiveness.

Beside them another fellow was welding the rolled steel into cylinders. I asked about his welder's mask.

"He has one but does not wear it," said Dangi. The welder went into the shop and returned wearing a pair of glasses before he continued to weld a few cylinders while we watched with our eyes closed, opening them only after the sound of the arcing had stopped.

The pumps were ready for painting and now went to another part of the shop where they got a coat of green paint. All the other IDE pumps I had seen were red and I asked about the color. The answer was that green paint was cheaper at this time. The more I thought about it, the more that seemed to be a reasonable answer. These pumps were going to farmers who had trouble raising the ten bucks for the purchase. They were probably more concerned about the price point than the color. It was not a matter of building an identifiable image. If the farmer could grow an extra crop in a year because of the irrigation, my bet is that he would remember the name and buy the same product. I don't think there is a lot of competition in the treadle pump business in Nepal under any conditions.

I headed outside to the huge pile of cement in front of the shop next door. I have always been amazed by masons. I have thought that if I were to be a craftsman it would be in the masonry business. A few minutes of watching the women mix cement with their hands and carry the large bowls to the back of the shop where it was being used to build an expansion to the shop, had me certain I would not be joining the masonry guild in Nepal.

It is a lot easier to visualize yourself working with stones and cement when you are sticking a few stones to a retaining wall in your back yard, than when you see the backbreaking labor these people put in day after day in their equivalent of the construction business.

I moved down the row of shops to where the pumps were being sold.

THE ANNAPURNA HIMALAYAN RANGE

POKHARA   nepal:

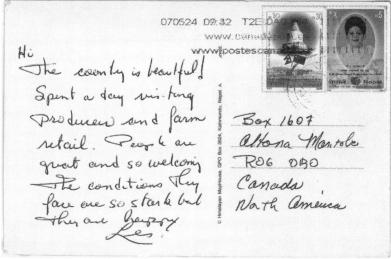

Hi
  The country is beautiful!
Spent a day visiting
producers and farm
retail. People are
great and so welcoming
The conditions they
face are so stark but
they are happy
  Les.

© Himalayan MapHouse, GPO Box 3924, Kathmandu, Nepal A

Box 1607
Altona Manitoba
R0G 0B0
Canada
North America

Selling pumps has changed peoples lives, but it is time for the next generation

Chapter 9
The Dealer

Our little delegation moved down the street. America may think that it developed the concept of the strip mall, but it appears that Nepal has mastered the concept. Every town has its main street lined with shop after shop sharing a common wall. The entire street has the appearance of a strip mall.

We made our way to a dealer who sold pumps manufactured at the welding shop we had just visited. A man I guessed to be in his mid 50's and wearing the traditional topi, approached and welcomed us.

The goods his store offered had spilled out into the yard and left no space in what would have been the parking lot in America. That was of little concern because customers were not arriving in 4 wheel drive pickup trucks. They walked or rode in an ox cart.

The front of his lot carried an assortment of plastic pipe that would become an irrigation system, and several pumps hanging from a pole cross member about six feet above the ground.

He told us that he had started the business 14 years ago. He began selling the treadle pumps as soon as they became available in the area. He currently sells 150 – 200 pumps a year. There are 13 other dealers in the area and if sales are spread evenly that means an additional 2,000 pumps a year that are finding their way to region's fields.

"Depending on the year," he said, "if it is a good year and farmers have money they will buy a pump. If there is no crop they cannot afford to buy a pump."

"The pumps have changed agriculture in our area. Now that they have pumps, farmers can grow vegetables. Seed production has increased with irrigation as well. Now farmers can grow seed."

He was not worried about the market being saturated with pumps. "When farmers have a pump they can irrigate, grow more crops and expand. They become better customers. They are back for another pump," he said.

He went on to explain that the addition of the treadle pumps has more impact on the community than just increasing farmers' production. Prior to irrigation, the dry season meant no production so vegetables had to be imported for food during this time.

"Previously at this time of year, bottle gourds would be 35 rupees per kilogram. Now they are produced locally and the farmers sell them for 7 rupees per kilogram, and that is a good return for them," he said. "The farmers are getting a good return and the people of the village have more affordable food."

We moved into the shop to sit and sip the mandatory tea. While we were having tea, the next generation of shop keeper arrived. The man's son had a business degree from the local college.

The look on my face must have revealed my surprise because without further questioning he explained that the town of 35,000 residents had a business college and a medical college as well. The fact that a medical training facility was located in this setting only added to my concern about sending people from around the world to evaluate the conditions. Why not use the money to provide jobs for the local people instead of using it for United Nations delegations.

My first thought was that the pumps these farmers were buying did more to better the conditions of Nepal than all the white SUV's with UN logos, but I am sure they play a role as well.

The younger man went on to explain that he was ready to take over the business. I looked at Dad and saw an unmistakable smile of pride. One of the greatest challenges in Canadian agriculture is succession planning. Yet both of the businesses I had visited today have a second generation ready to take over the business, and there is a plan in place for further expansion. I came here thinking Nepalese agriculture was decades behind Canadian agriculture. Now I am not so sure. There might be more than a few things that we could adopt from their systems.

The plan was to expand into a full line of farm supplies. Obviously, as tractors became more prevalent in the area he would carry the implements they used in addition to the shears he currently had for plows pulled by oxen or water buffalo. Gradually the implements of mechanization would replace the shovels and spades.

His plan seemed solid, one that would be accepted by a banker, but his plan was not to go to a bank. Rather, he intended to expand slowly as he could afford it by reinvesting the profits generated from the goods already sold.

There was another lesson we could apply to Canadian

agriculture or society as a whole: the idea of living within one's means.

On the way out I stopped to look at the long handled spades. I was surprised that they bore the name of the manufacturer SADA stamped into the business end of the tool. I thought that would cause a problem with dirt sticking to it. I mentioned it to Surendra. He agreed. It was the idea of some marketing guru to stamp the name of the company on the shovel. I am sure that when the mud was sticking to it during use, it would not conjure up positive thoughts for the user as he had to remove the sticking soil.

We got back in the car and were heading off, when Surendra offered more information about the value of the pumps.

"What the dealer said is precisely true," he said. "The pumps not only bring the added income that you see, they have changed the life of these people. Now the men stay at home to raise another crop. They used to leave to try and find work."

"Where did they go?" I asked.

"Anywhere. Many of them went to India. The Nepalese have a good reputation as workers in India, so they would go there and work in the vegetable fields to make some money to support their families."

He went on to tell me the story of a young girl who had stopped by the IDE display during one of the demonstrations. She told him how happy she was now that they had a pump and could grow vegetables. "Now my dad can stay home and grow another crop," she said.

I had never thought of India as a place to go to find work, especially for stoop labor. I thought of it as a place that had more than enough labor, but everything is relative.

"It is easy to find a job, especially during the potato harvest," he said. "Nearly every Nepalese family has someone working outside the country who is sending money home. Many of those people are working in conditions that you would think would not allow them to save extra money."

We continued to weave our way down the road. The

76

traffic was a mix of ox carts, UN vehicles, bicycles and people walking to and from the local market. A population of 35,000 does generate some traffic.

I asked how close we were to the Indian border. Surendra replied that it was less than 20 kilometers away and asked if I would like to go.

Twenty kilometers on rural Nepalese roads is further than on Canadian roads, but I could not turn down an opportunity like this.

"Can we?" I asked with the enthusiasm of a kid going to the circus. I had no idea how accurate the comparison would be. When we got to the border crossing, a circus is the only thing I could compare it to.

As we neared the border crossing point, the road became more congested with every type of vehicle imaginable. Horses seemed to replace oxen as the most popular means of animal power, but suddenly we were in a traffic jam of fuel trucks.

Surendra explained that fuel rationing meant black markets and smuggling. I told him I was aware of how the free market functioned. He laughed when I told him the story of a friend who works at the Mexico-US border and says he used to be a smuggler. Now he is considered a logistics expert and claims to be the guy who invented "just in time" delivery.

The tanker trucks were delivering fuel that had been bought under rationing conditions and would be sold on the open/black market. Either way, the road was more of a parking lot than a highway.

The border to India was marked by a rather ostentatious gate. People walked back and forth, crossing freely from Nepal to India. For a split second I considered the idea of visiting India. Surendra read my mind.

"They would stop you in a second," he said. "They do not do anything to the Indians or us, but someone of your color could not walk across without being stopped."

He then pointed to the police station that had been bombed by the Maoist Insurgents a few months earlier. "Our soldiers ran across the border so they would not be killed." He said in disgust. "That is the way they protect our country when the fighting starts. They flee to India knowing they will not be followed."

We talked some more about the political situation. I had already gathered from the English language newspapers that it was not good. The parliament with a split of eight parties was virtually ineffective. No one would agree to anything, even things as basic as the format the discussion should take.

Surendra told me the majority of the country was safe. There were only a few hotspots where the insurgents were staging open resistance.

Adding political instability to the list of factors that keep things from being accomplished, the progress of these people, and what appears to be some degree of optimism for a better future, is amazing considering the conditions they face.

I wonder how Canadians would fare in these conditions. We complain about the things we have at home.

I settled into the back seat thinking, as I so often have, that I live in the best place on earth, a place where we take so much for granted and complain so much about so little.

HRH THE DALAI LAMA

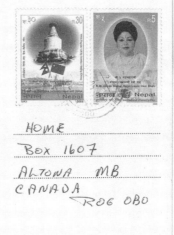

Hi
- It is wedding season here, so weddings everywhere - if they don't get married by this weekend they have to wait until October - so there is a big rush this week
fs

HOME
BOX 1607
ALTONA MB
CANADA
R0G 0B0

A local market provides a better return then selling to a wholesaler

Chapter 10
The Marketplace

To the untrained eye it looks like a couple of cement pads with steel corrugated roofs crowded up against a country road. To the people of the Vegetable Co-operative, it is the center of their marketing efforts allowing them to get more for their produce. Instead of selling to dealers who transport the vegetables to town and receive a better price, the producers are able to sell at the local market and get the retail price.

Kamala Napalle is the chairperson of the co-operative and she sees it as a good beginning.

"Someday I hope we can have a collection facility here," she said, "so the producers can gather their vegetables and sell them together for the market in the city."

She does not downplay the impact of the stand beside the dusty road.

"Retail prices are always better than wholesale," she said. "This gives us the opportunity to get more for our produce, but we cannot sell everything here. As production increases we will need to look at other markets. We need to act together to get better prices for our vegetables."

Napalle is a mother of two. She is also the marketing expertise behind the current success, but like any true entrepreneur there is always another challenge, a way to grow the business and get a better return.

Someone with her marketing savvy could move on and make much more money in a marketing position anywhere, but she has chosen to stay in her village and work for the betterment of the local people.

Her enterprising spirit comes though in almost everything she says. It seems at odds with her role as the chairperson of a co-operative, but she has no problem justifying the roles.

"One has to put back into the community. If you want to gain something you have to sacrifice something," she said.

Napalle credits her mother with getting her started in the co-operative movement.

"My mother was always involved in co-operatives," she says. "I grew up with them and it was only natural that I

got involved and things have continued to grow. I was an ordinary housewife with a small mobile shop and very little confidence, but now because of the success we have had with our co-operative, I have people from other institutions calling me for advice."

Napelle did not appear short of confidence when she talked about the future of the co-operative or her own future. She is dedicated to bringing about change.

"I want to become involved in politics," she said. "We need

people to change our country and I believe I can help with that."

She was hesitant when asked about a political figure that she would consider a role model. The country's conflicts with India will not allow her to choose Indira Gandhi and she laughs when a comparison to Margaret Thatcher is made.

"I would say that I have always been a radical," she said, "I believe in change." It was a major change in the co-operative that brought about the successes.

"When the co-op was formed we had an executive of all men, and it failed. We elected another executive of only

men and the co-op went broke again. There was no transparency and everyone was trying to line their own pockets, so we decided to elect only women. We have done much better since then."

She said it was not easy breaking into the traditionally

man's world of marketing, but in Nepal as everywhere else, nothing succeeds like success.

"We started to have some success and people started to listen to me. As I was able to get more information and make better decisions we made more money, and people began to trust my decisions," she says.

While we sat on the grass behind the market and chatted about co-operatives and her own future, another woman sat close by and offered a few comments. A half dozen men sat in a semicircle around us, never offering a word. They seemed quite content to spend the afternoon sitting in the shade of the trees.

The Market is located on property owned by the local school. The money paid for rent is used for maintenance on the school facilities but Napelle is hopeful that she will be able to negotiate a lower price for the land in the next agreement.

The current agreement is for 3,000 square meters for twenty years. She would like to expand the area and extend the agreement to fifty years. Small vendors are charged a fee of five rupees for the day, while large ones pay ten rupees. Forty percent of the revenue goes to the school and sixty percent remains with the co-operative.

The expanded size and permanence would allow for expansion of the facility and for the rental of space to some outside vendors.

"Our first obligation is to our members and to have them selling their product," she said, "but I would like to have outside vendors that we could charge for space. We could have spice vendors who would provide a revenue source for us. With that money we could build the collection depot we need for our vegetables so that we can ship them to the market in the city."

The role of chair of the co-operative is purely volunteer. She receives no payment for the time she spends on "company business". She relies on the vegetables that she grows and sells in the marketplace for her income. She admits to having begun a bit of trading in the vegetable business and brokering some vegetables into the city market

"I need to know how the market works so that we can be ready for the day when we have our collection facility and want to sell our vegetables. I have begun to trade a few vegetables in order to get a better understanding of the business," she said. I know that she will not be taken advantage of on these trades. When she is ready to enter the larger arena with her co-operative's crops, farmers can count on getting the best price that she can negotiate. The problem is that they might lose her to the legislature in the near future.

On the way out of the market I stopped to watch a youngster rolling leaves of the betel tree. He had a selection of leaves and substances for the centre of the wad. He made up a chew to comply with the customer's requests.

It is an art form that appears everywhere. A person can purchase a small wad of the leaf wrapped around his choice of flavoring. He places it in his mouth, similar to the way a cowboy handles chewing tobacco. The difference is that the saliva emitted after chewing the betel leaf is bright red, almost blood-like, in color.

The art form is being able to spit without getting any of the red color on his own clothes, a task most have mastered.

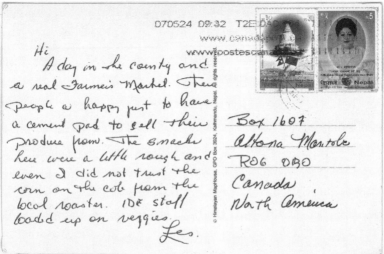

Hi
A day in the county and
a real Farmers Market. There
people a happy just to have
a cement pad to sell their
produce from. The snacks
here were a little rough and
even I did not trust the
corn on the cob from the
local roaster. 10¢ stall
loaded up on veggies.
Les.

Box 1697
Altona Manitoba
R0G 0B0
Canada
North America

Coffee plants take 4 years to harvest, but are the way of the future

Chapter 11
The Coffee Nursery

J oe had no intention of being the operator of a coffee nursery. He was content with his job in the Nepalese education system, looking forward to retirement and spending more time in his orange grove.

Today though, his nursery generates 1,700 plants a year that are intended for his plantation and for local farmers who are expanding the country's coffee production.

Why did he get started in coffee production when he was approaching retirement?

"The people from IDE asked me to get started in coffee," he says with a smile and a wave of his hand toward the young trees and the shelter which provides shade for the seedlings.

Emerging coffee plants take nearly 60 days before the first leaf is formed. The tiny shoot carries the cotyledons to the top of the plant. During this time it is critical that the plant be protected from the sun.

Joe had established beds that are covered with straw to protect the emerging shoots. As they grow to the stage of having leaves, he transplants the seedlings into plastic bags where they remain for another 18 months before they are ready to be placed in the field. The beds are a mixture of manure and coarse soil that allows for internal drainage and are covered with leaves to provide shade in the early stages. When the seedlings emerge through the mulch, they are transplanted.

While a coffee seedling costs only a few cents, a plantation is a major investment for a farmer in Nepal, where cash flow is always a problem. The first harvest is 5 years away from the purchase of a seedling.

Joe said that while the initial request from IDE for him to get started in coffee came as a surprise, when he evaluated the crop it was obviously a good fit.

"It can be intercropped with oranges which are high. The coffee fits in the middle and you can grow vegetables below," he says. The land he farms is steep hillsides, terraced in strips which are little more than a meter wide.

His farm is at an elevation of 900 meters above sea level, just about the minimum requirement for the production of the high quality coffee that Nepal has targeted. All the production in the country is Arabica beans which are produced above 800 meters. Lower quality beans such as Robusta can be produced at lower altitudes and provide a greater yield, but the price on the world market is considerably lower.

The coffee industry of Nepal has decided to target the affluent coffee drinkers of Japan and America by producing a high quality crop grown organically.

Support groups have developed a plan for starting local nurseries like Joe's to develop the industry in the country's mountainous region.

"Transportation is expensive, so they asked me to start a nursery for farmers in this area," says Joe. "That way farmers can have access to the plants and not have the added expense

of having to transport seedlings from a nursery far away." The policy has meant the development of several small coffee nurseries which reduce transportation costs. The nurseries also allow farmers to get experience with the crop before they begin their own plantations, a critical factor in a country where delivery of agricultural extension is difficult at best.

IDE has helped to establish 22 nurseries in remote areas which it has targeted for expansion of the coffee industry. The nurseries not only spread the risk of crop failures, they also provide learning centers for farmers in the areas where production is expected to expand. Farmers can observe the crop growing before they make the investment in seedlings and plant the trees on their own land.

While the government has established extension offices,

government employees are most likely to work with individuals in their immediate area, particularly when they see that the individual has taken some initiative and organizations like IDE Maps are involved to provide some support as well.

Joe is in his third year. He now has plants that are ready to go to the mountainside. Ideally the plants are placed two meters apart, a space that can be difficult to achieve on the narrow terraces.

He may be ready to retire from his government job, but Joe attacks the coffee industry like a man half his age. Coffee plants take five years before the first harvest and then yield substantial crops for 20 years. In some cases a plantation may last as long as 60 years, but that is under ideal conditions and tender loving care.

"We will get a plantation established and it will need care," he says. "To keep it producing you must be replacing trees and trimming and working with the trees all the time." Coffee only produces fruit from the vertical branches, so there is no reason to let the plant spread to great width. The leaves are best kept in the shade, so coffee provides an excellent companion crop for his tangerine orchards.

ANNAPURNA SOUTH

Machhapuchhre Base Camp

Nepal

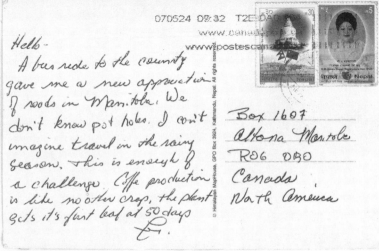

Hello –
A bus ride to the country gave me a new appreciation of roads in Manitoba. We don't know pot holes. I can't imagine travel in the rainy season. This is enough of a challenge. Coffee production is like no other crop, the plant gets it's first leaf at 50 days

Box 1607
Altona Manitoba
R0G 0B0
Canada
North America

A new pump means another crop of vegetables

Chapter 12
Women Vegetable Growers

I t's a problem seldom faced by North American organizations, but it is a very real problem in rural Nepal.

How do you elect a functioning executive to serve as volunteers? North Americans claim they don't have the time, but when only four of your members can read and write the problem is even more serious. That is precisely the situation facing the Jagriti Mahila Multipurpose Co-operative.

The group has 38 members, all female, who produce vegetables for the market in their village and to sell to wholesalers for shipment to cities like Kathmandu.

Munni Devi Kaulik is the chairperson of the co-operative. She says that while the group has been successful in bettering the situation of its members, it is a challenge to get people to take a leadership role. The group has been in existence for two years and has brought significant changes to village life.

"We have a feeling of independence now. We are not as dependant on our husbands," she said. "We can earn a living."

The feeling of independence is valuable, but soon the practical problems of the situation hit home.

"These women are working in the fields and raising children as well as doing many things in the village," she said. "One can only devote so much time to serve on the executive of the Co-op. Only four of our members can read and write." The co-operative offers literacy classes that run for three months, it they also puts more demands on the time of the already overloaded women.

While I spoke to Kaulik, three more women arrived and made their way into the dark room at the back of house. They sat quietly on the floor in the stifling heat and humidity. They shared a fan, and created some air movement by rotating it rather than the waving motion that is used in North America.

"We have money to send our children to school," answered one, when I asked what difference the co-operative had made in their lives. Eighty farmer members had purchased the IDE treadle pumps through the co-operative.

"The pumps have allowed us to grow another crop,"

said another of the women. "That is extra income. Now we have income year-round and vegetables for ourselves."

The classes focus on enabling the members to keep records for themselves and other agri-businesses. The result is empowerment of the members .

I sat back and looked at the surroundings. We were in the most basic of living conditions, immaculately clean. No doubt a special effort had been made because I was visiting. These women were telling me that the small pumps had made the difference in their lives of being able to earn a living, and giving them a feeling of independence. Now the co-operative was teaching them to read. I wondered if they had any idea of what kind of empowerment that would bring, and the joy that would come with it. I also wondered when they would find time to read between raising vegetables and kids, getting water from the well and cooking meals and the other endless tasks that come along with being a woman in a developing country.

What did they think of my continuous scribbling in the note book that I take everywhere?

That night as I went over my notes, I thought about the skill of reading and how wc takc it for granted. These women were not talking about reading to learn the news, as I look forward to my newspaper or reading for enjoyment as I do in my big arm chair on a slow Sunday afternoon. They were talking about being able to keep records so as not to get cheated by the merchants that buy their produce. They were talking about a skill that would allow them to have a say in their own business.

They were a lot closer to understanding the value of the skill than I was.

We talked for the better part of an hour about what the co-operative meant in their lives and in the life of the village. It seemed that their feelings varied from embarrassment at their lack of literacy to pride at taking the initiative to better their lives. I could not help but feel envy for their dedication. I wished that I had as much dedication to what I was doing, and that I would work as hard to make the world a better place for my kids.

I kept thinking that we have become complacent in our wealth in North America. If only we would work as hard as these people. With the opportunities and the resources we take for granted in North America, imagine the results we would see.

Talk shifted from the challenges of running the co-operative to the agronomic practices the group used in their vegetable production. The women purchased some of their seeds from the local Agro Vet store and saved some of their own from open pollinated varieties.

"Where there is a benefit in hybrid seed, we purchase it from Agro Vet," said Kuliak. "Some of the other varieties we

keep our own seed." The advantage to the hybrid seed is not only higher-yielding, but also earlier maturing crops, which in the vegetable business means everything. The first crop to market commands the best prices, in Nepal or Altona, Manitoba.

It was time to take a look at the fields. As we made our way through the village, it was obvious that the town pump was the center of activity.

Children were playing at the pump, and some women were washing clothes. Others were carrying water home for the daily family requirements.

We walked out to the plots that were separated by little dikes, which obviously were meant to mark the property line as well as hold the valuable water in.

In one area a lone woman was picking chilies. In another, a man was tending to his tomatoes. Across the road, a group of women and children were picking chilies. A gate kept the wandering goats from dining on the greenery.

The area was about two acres in size and offered a microcosm of the country I had seen. Where the IDE pumps provided water for the fields, vegetables were green and being picked. The small plots were a hub of activity.

Other plots had no water and the soil was concrete hard, baked by the unrelenting heat.

A little further away, some people were putting up hay in small stacks, while children played at the end of the field. The hay was closer to what North American farmers would use for bedding their cattle than feeding them, but it was the best these producers could do in the conditions they had.

It was all visible within a few hundred yards: the poverty, the work, the struggles and then the changes that came about by just adding water.

I was ready to go back to my hotel and digest what I had

seen. These women, who not only spend their days in the fields raising crops and kids, were also trying to better themselves with literacy classes in the evenings. I would spend my evening thinking about the day. They would spend their evening doing their homework and practicing their reading.

We got into the car and headed back into the city. As though I had not had enough experiences for the day, the traffic served to make me more aware of the differences in the way we lived. People crowded onto buses on their way home from a job that would pay them barely enough to live, much less enjoy the standard of living we take for granted.

Riding in the back seat with the window open, I was caught between the fumes of a bus idling beside us and motorcycles and bicycles weaving their way through the lane on the right hand side of the car. When the bus driver got out and came to the back of the bus, I thought it was a strange place for a tune up. He opened the grill on the back of the bus, reached into the compartment, and pulled out a goat.

It was not the engine compartment at all, but rather where the goats rode on the trip into town. I was still busy exclaiming about the goat passenger to Surendra when the driver reached in and pulled out another goat, and then one more. He let the

animals down on the street. The owner came from around the front of the bus, took the short leash that was connected to the collar and led them down the sidewalk.

We were nowhere near a livestock market as best I could

tell and yet this man walked down the sidewalk with three goats. Perhaps it was barbecue time. I have no idea how they ended up, but it was just another lesson about how different some parts of the world are.

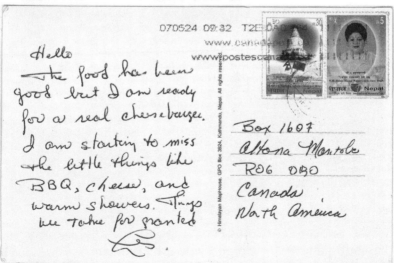

Hello
~~the~~ food has been good but I am ready for a real cheeseburger. I am starting to miss the little things like BBQ, cheese, and warm showers. Things we take for granted

Box 1607
Altona Manitoba
R0G 0B0
Canada
North America

070524 09:32 T2E DA
www.canad
www.postesca

Irrigation allows for a high value crop like chili

Chapter 13
Chili Producer

We arrived in Khajura and made our way to Sanchem Guest House and checked in. This place was one of the most rustic places I have stayed at in all of my travels. The lobby was no more than six feet wide and the registration desk took up half of that for the first four feet inside the door. A row of four chairs sat against the opposite wall.

Surendra and I went through the registration drill with every piece of identification I had, including my passport. The lobby was deserted and I decided to take a few pictures of the street while Surendra completed the registration. I returned to find three fellows seated on the chairs in the lobby, watching the TV mounted in the corner. I didn't like how close they were to my luggage so I made a point of getting it behind the desk and we were off.

We went outside and were met by some staff from Winrock. Our group had now swelled to a half-dozen. We tried in vain to negotiate a couple of taxis to take us out to the farms where we were to see some chili production. The process was not working and half of the fellows from the local office decided to head back to work. Three of us could fit in one car but still no luck finding a taxi. We were on the sidewalk so long that a bird thought I was a statue and made a deposit on my hat; not a highlight of the day, but it did wash off.

Finally, after being refused by about 8 cars, we decided to take the local bus. We could do that for a few pennies and have them stop right next to the field. I was up for the adventure of a local bus ride, and we climbed aboard.

Surendra was already aware of my claustrophobia and suggested I take the seat at the back of the bus because that allowed me the entire aisleway and less cramped conditions. It was a good choice. As in most parts of the world, the back of the bus is not a coveted position. Judging by the looks I got as we entered the bus, not many tourists take the bus in rural Nepal. I wasn't too worried about that and settled in. It wasn't long before I slid over to a seat by the window and was taking pictures of people outside the bus and buying snacks from vendors at stops along the way. I considered it a part of the Nepalese experience and escaped none the worse for wear.

We reached the chili field in about a half hour. I was amazed at what a popular stop it was. I didn't think it was a scheduled stop, but six guys got out with us. I was commenting to Surendra about its popularity when he laughed and pointed back at the bus. It turns out that this is where a rest stop should have been built if they had them in Nepal. The fellows completed their inspection of the roadside vegetation and got back on the bus. We continued down the hill to an area of chili production.

The area was a hundred feet or more below the grade of the road. It would have been a comfortable descent for a mountain goat. For an overweight Canadian it was incredibly steep, but I made it down without mishap.

The IDE staff in the area showed us the plots of chilies. The chili crop was an added bonus. Last year during the dry season this land had yielded nothing, but this year it was a garden of chili plants in neat rows. Farmers had told me earlier that chilies are one of the highest value crops they could produce. This field was now yielding what to me looked like a bumper crop. It was impressive indeed.

I was putting my camera back in my shoulder bag when I noticed that my travel wallet was missing. That was the large document folder that held my passport and airline tickets. I always kept it in the side pocket of my shoulder bag and it was not there now. I tried to convince myself that I had put it in my suitcase when I was done with it at the hotel. It was a vain attempt and did little to alleviate the sinking feeling in my stomach.

We climbed back up the hill and walked down the road to our next stop, a multi use water system. We passed through a village that was in the middle of a marriage ceremony.

It was indeed wedding season in Nepal and time for celebration, but not all tears shed at a wedding are tears of joy. We made our way through the village and were beginning another descent when we came upon the bride and a group of her family huddled in a tight group and crying seriously.

I asked Surendra about the marriage and what would bring about this reaction. He explained that it was not a sad event, but that bride might be feeling some sadness at leaving her family. The family members would also be sharing the same feelings.

"She will be going to the village of her husband," he said. "It may not be close by and she may feel that she will not see her family for along time." I had just experienced the travel conditions of rural Nepal and could understand her concern.

The noise of the celebration continued on the road above us in stark contrast to the sadness I saw on the face of this young lady as she held tight to her family behind the buildings.

105

The drums and tin horns continued to play what I assumed was a traditional wedding tune in Nepal, but they were not doing much to alleviate the concern of this bride.

We continued down the hill until we came to a farmyard stuck on the side of the hill. The steepness of the hill meant that even the yard itself was terraced and spread over several levels.

A girl about ten years old was getting water from a tap mounted on a pole outside the house. Surendra explained that in the last year the farm had been the recipient of a multi use water system. That meant water for drinking and irrigation. The addition of an extra holding tank meant the family now had water for household use and also to irrigate its vegetable crops: a life changing event.

"It is not that there is a shortage of water," he said, "but during the wet season it runs away and during the dry season there is not enough. Now they can fill the tanks and store enough water that comes down the mountain."

We made our way to the next level down and were going through what I thought was the frame of a greenhouse when Surendra explained the framework to me.

"It is covered with mesh, and it protects the tomatoes from damage by hail," he said. "This area gets much hail and

it damages the crop so they cover it with mesh and it still gets the sunlight.

The visit was a good one but I could do little to resolve my fears of being a traveler without a passport. I told Surendra that I noticed my folder was missing from its usual spot. We turned back up the hill and caught the next bus into town. No matter how often I went through my bag I could not find the folder. It was gone and I indeed was without a passport or my airline tickets home.

We went back to the room and I checked my suitcase. It too did not yield the travel portfolio that contained my passport. I immediately thought of the three characters who had appeared from nowhere when I was registering in the morning. They had not been there a minute before, but when I came back from taking pictures they were sitting much too close to my bags.

The passport and tickets would be of no use to them but they must have assumed that the portfolio would contain some cash. Sorry fellows, I know better than that and I should have known better than to leave my bag unattended for even a heartbeat.

I have been down this road before and know that you need a police form from the jurisdiction where the event occurs. That, Surendra informed me, was going to be a little more difficult than I might think.

"You will have to write a letter explaining what happened" he said. "It might be better if you said you lost it because if you say it was stolen then there was a crime and the police will have to investigate and they cannot give you the letter until they do the investigation. Since we need it tomorrow, just say it was lost in the field and we can get going."

It was not the system that I was used to, but it was his country and in the two weeks of travel I had gained tremendous respect for this fellow. I sat down to write the letter as he suggested.

Letter completed, we walked to the police station to begin the process.

"You will have to come back tomorrow," said the little man with the big attitude who listened to my story and then offered that bit of advice. I started to say that I thought it would be best to report he incident as soon as it happened. Surendra slowed me down and said we would be back in the morning.

"Things are different here. This is not North America." He was right. I was trying to apply the rules of my country in someone else's sandbox. I know better than that, but I got caught thinking that I knew what was logical. Not so.

It was logical that the Lost Department would be open tomorrow at ten and I would be best to be back then. I agreed.

We returned to the hotel for a less than satisfactory dining experience and a few adult beverages before calling it a night. There was nothing more I was going to do tonight.

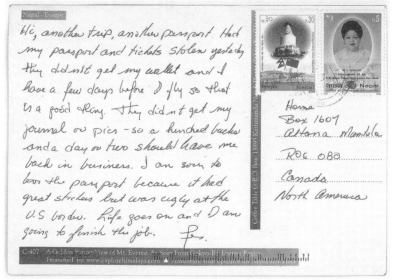

Lake Pokhara, world class hotels in a remote setting

Chapter 14
Pokhara

I woke up at 5 a.m. without the aid of an alarm and had a "sort of" shower. This was one of the few times I was glad for the lack of water pressure. I didn't realize water could be that cold, without freezing, but it truly was. I used yesterday's t-shirt to dry off. It was only later that Surendra explained that you had to ask for a towel and toilet paper at the front desk. Apparently he had made the same mistake. It was not that the hotel didn't supply them, it was just that you had to ask for them.

Shower completed, but not completely dry, I headed downstairs for coffee and to write some cards. I didn't like the feeling of being in a hotel room with a deadbolt on the outside. It was not that I suspected that someone would lock me in and then light the place on fire, but I just thought it was somewhat unusual that you would need a deadbolt on the outside of a hotel room. It seemed to be like asking for a prankster to lock someone in their room.

I finished my cards and applied the stamps before realizing that I had put the wrong denominations on them. It was 30 rupees for an international card. I had bought the 5 rupee stamps because of the image of Mount Everest, but now they were on the cards. I added the 30 rupee stamps to most of them and deposited them all in the mail box, (the ones with only the 5 rupee stamps never did make it to Canada).

Surendra arrived and we rewrote the report that the police would require. We wanted to be ready for the office to open at ten o'clock. We went over to a business center that looked a lot like a phone booth, but it had a telephone, internet and fax machine available. Deepak at the IDE office in Kathmandu informed us of the process required and faxed us the forms so that I could complete the process without being in Kathmandu. Time was of the essence if I hoped to get this done and return home on time.

Deepak contacted the Canadian office and faxed the forms. This guy was a life saver.

We headed over to the police station. Surendra asked if I had a stamp. I thought it was a strange question, but he told me that the document would not be official until it had a stamp. I pulled out my remaining 30 rupee stamps and was about to stick one on the paper.

"No," he said, "Not such an expensive one. That is a waste. Don't you have anything smaller?" At this point I wasn't worried about a couple of cents on a stamp that would make my document official. The stamp stuck and the job was done.

Surendra had coached me in the fine art of police expedience, saying that if I reported a theft it could be days until we had a report. If I said I had lost my passport we could get a paper saying that I had lost my documents and we would be done in an hour.

As mentioned earlier, if I said that it was stolen that would mean a crime had been committed and there would need to be an investigation and all kinds of delays. I went with the lost documents story and finished my report before we headed over to the police station for the opening.

We arrived before most officers did. We were asked to wait outside. We told our story to the same two fellows we had talked to the night before, same guys, same story. Eventually we were invited inside and shown into a room with two young officers sitting behind tables. One was checking the soccer scores in the paper, the other one was waiting for us. On the way in we passed through a room where I assumed there was a court proceeding. They explained later that it was a community committee and complainants could bring their concerns. The police would listen and suggest a mutually agreeable resolution. All of this, I am sure, was done without any written work.

We retold the story for the third time and waited an appropriate time before being asked to go upstairs and tell the story to the commanding officer.

I was getting good at the story by now. After my fourth go at it, the commander looked at me and said, "What do you want us to do?"

I told him that I would need a police report to replace my passport and file an insurance claim. I was hopeful his office could provide such a report. He seemed unaware of the

process. This appeared to be the first time he had had a request for a police report. Back downstairs we went, to the same fellow as time three. We repeated the story and he translated it to a young fellow with a clipboard who made endless notes, then disappeared. The young officer assured me the report was coming. I heard banging in the next room that had me remembering the old Flintstone cartoons where the fellow engraved the newspaper with a hammer and chisel. A peek into the room revealed that the young man with the clipboard was now at a manual typewriter with a carriage at least 24 inches wide, and banging out my report.

The young fellow returned with the typed document and gave me the second copy, keeping the original. It had been a long time since I had seen carbon paper, but it is alive and well and working in the Nepalese police system.

I got my copy of the letter, and we headed out to find a taxi that would take us to Pokhara. I checked my watch and found that we had only spent an hour and a half in the police station. It seemed like so much longer, but in reality this was still the same morning that we had entered it.

Surendra negotiated a cab to Pokhara and we were off on what would have been a very enjoyable drive had I not

been so concerned about getting this paperwork done in time to catch my scheduled flight home.

Pokhara is a place of incredible beauty. Its altitude (827 m) is slightly less than Kathmandu. It records the highest rainfall in the country, averaging over 150 inches annually.

It was once a stop on the vibrant trade route between India and Tibet. While that has long ago disappeared, it is still a trading center for the people of this remote area of the Himalayas. Two ethnic groups from the area have established  worldwide reputations. The Thakalis are known for their entrepeneurship, and the Gurkha soldiers have established a reputation as warriors. To this day the British Army maintains a Gurkha unit.

"It is a prime job to get into the British army" says Surendra, "Young men enlist in the British Army and spend time in England and are able to retire relatively wealthy on their army pensions."

In June of 2007, the British Army announced that it would be accepting women to serve in the unit. It was inundated with applications. Women cited the army wages, about one hundred times more than they could earn at civilian jobs, and the pension plan of the military as the main reasons for their applications.

I was more than a little concerned about getting to the Capital and getting the wheels turning on the paperwork I required. Surendra was insistent that we had done all we could and a night in Pokhara was what I needed more than anything. I gave in to his insistence and was glad that I had.

He was familiar with the city, having spent several years working there in a bank. That had only been five years earlier, but the city had changed dramatically. However, it still had the laid back feeling of a resort town. The view of the lake on one side and the mountains on the other, made it impossible not to put away the concerns of government paperwork and enjoy the view.

We checked into the Trek-o-tel. I was feeling better already. It is a world class resort with beautiful rooms and a shower I knew would work, but that was for the morning. It was time to head uptown and get some lunch. We walked up the main street. While it was lined with shops selling every type of camping gear and offering trekking and hiking, it lacked

 the aggressiveness of Tamil. It was an attitude of 'come in if you like' rather than 'raw meat in the shark tank' and I quite enjoyed it.

The Boomerang Restaurant caught our attention. We found a place on the patio overlooking the lake and settled in. I ordered a cheeseburger, the only food that you can eat anytime of the day or night, and was enjoying the scenery when Surendra's cell phone rang. It was the consulate office. My paperwork had come through and they needed the names of two people, non-relatives, who could vouch for my existence. Oh, and they needed a home and an office phone number for both. And, they had to have known me for at least two years.

I am not good with phone numbers at the best of times, but in this situation I was stumped. Who could I think of that would answer a call from Nepal and say that I was who I said I was. I gave the consulate the number of the radio station I used to work at, and the names of two fellows there whose home numbers I could remember. I remembered one because his daughter used to baby-sit for us. The other had been a friend since high school. Twenty years of curling with him meant that his home number was one of the few burned in my brain, or retrievable at this time. Mission complete. They would call to verify the information I had given them, and I could come by the office when I got back to Kathmandu and get my emergency passport.

I turned back to the matter at hand, my cheeseburger and a cold drink.

Surendra told me of the changes in the town and how it had been transformed from a sleepy village to a city of 100,000 in five years. We went down to walk along the lake and saw a pipeline from each hotel drawing water from the lake. I am sure there were outlet lines as well, but they were more discreetly covered.

We watched some people crowd into a boat and head over to the Barahi Temple. It was a two story Pagoda dedicated to the boar manifestation of Ajima, the protectress of the female voice of Shakti. I didn't know how they could squeeze even another chicken into the boats, but apparently on Saturdays people take animals and birds with them to be sacrificed to the deity.

We strolled the street and I wandered into a shop to look at some of the handiwork.

"It is really Yak," said the young man, already combing it with a comb he pulled from his back pocket. Before I could offer a reply he pulled out a lighter and lit the wad of hair.

"Smell that," he said, "that is real Yak. It smells like your hair when it burns. It is Yak hair. It is real." I was sure the odor was real. Yak or not, it really stunk. I worked him on the price for awhile and bought one.

As we left the shop Surendra pointed across the street. "That is the bank I used to work in. I am going to say hello." I agreed to stay close by to visit a few shops and take a few pictures while he said his hellos.

I stepped into a print shop beside the bank, more to kill time than to purchase artwork. Before I knew it I was engaged in haggling over a couple of prints that featured elephants and "gold thread."

We went through the entire bargaining dance. The prints that started at 3,000 rupees were down to 800 and I said yes. The young man wrapped them careful. As he placed the roll in my hand he said, "nine hundred."

I mentioned that we had agreed on 800. He said we had, but they were really 900. I told him to put the prints in a dark place. I was well past annoyed as I left the shop and headed back to the bank steps to wait for Surendra. The young fellow followed me out of the shop and said that he would accept the 800. I said "no," or something to that effect.

In a few minutes Surendra appeared and I told him my story, and how I felt that the man had gone back on his word. I felt it was a skin tax issue, and he was just taking advantage of a tourist.

"No, that is the problem here," he said. "That is done all too often in business." We went back to the shop and bought the prints for 800 rupees.

On the walk back to the hotel, I could not help but wonder how this would work in the international arena, but perhaps that is the way business is done and we in Canada are naive in our reliance on written contracts. Much of the world is more concerned about bargaining ploys than being bound by a fixed contract.

Hi
Enjoyed a day at Lake Pokal. I have the paper work started for a new passport but it was good to take a breather. Pokal in the Nepal Banff. Nice view - lots of shops and a cheeseburger
Les

Home
Box 1607
Altona   Manitoba
Canada   R0G 0B0

Deep fried dumplings are the perfect snack when shopping in Patan

The drive from Pokhara took all of the morning. I dropped off my documents at the passport office, headed to my hotel and began working on some notes. It wasn't long before I realized that I could do that when I got home and that I would probably only visit Kathmandu once in my lifetime, so I had best get out and see it while I was here. At least that was the excuse I used to justify leaving the notes and heading uptown.

The guide books, and everyone else, told me that Patan was a must see, so I decided that would be my destination for the evening. The lady at the front desk of my hotel said it was about a twenty-minute walk. It turned out to be about twice that, but was well worth the effort. The experiences along the way added to the event.

Patan is one of the three major cities of Nepal and lies within the Municipality of Lalitpur. Lalitpur was founded in the third century B.C. by the Kirat dynasty and later expanded by Licchavis in the sixth century. The name is credited to the legend of the god Rato Machhindranath who was brought to the valley from Kamarou Kamachhya located in Assam, India by three people representing the three kingdoms of the Kathmandu Valley. One of them, Lalit, a farmer, carried god Rato Machhindranath to the valley all the way from Assam, the purpose being to overcome the worst drought in the valley.

The belief was that the god would make it rain in the valley. The town carries the name of the farmer, Lalit, and the suffix pur, meaning township.

Patan is considered the oldest and most beautiful of the three royal cities in the Kathmandu Valley, Kathmandu, Patan, and Bhaktapur. Urban sprawl and refugee camps mean there is little to distinguish one city from the other, but for locals there is still a distinction. As mentioned in an earlier chapter, these are not technically refugee camps, because to qualify for refugee status people must have crossed an international border.

Armed with my week old, well-wrinkled map, I headed off to the city known as the heart of arts and culture for the Kathmandu Valley. After about ten minutes of walking and not seeing any change in the character of the city around me, I decided to ask for more directions. A couple of transplanted

Americans out jogging informed me I was indeed on the right track, so I carried on.

It was not long before a vehicle pulled in front of me and a young lady seemed to fall out of the passenger's door. While she was straightening herself and gathering her thoughts, I seized the opportunity to confirm that I was on the road to Patan. She spoke perfect English, studied my map for a few minutes then looked at least three directions, appearing to get her bearings, smiled and said, "I need my spectacles."

Amazingly, when she was equipped with her glasses the map study did not take nearly as long. Her directions were precise and with pinpoint accuracy, "Cross that bridge, carry on past the temple and it can't be more than 15 minutes." I guess the lady at the hotel was a speed walker because I had been pounding the pavement much longer than 5 minutes.

I carried on and could not believe my luck when I came upon a tourist information booth that was open. It was surrounded by a locked fence, but there was a gentleman at the desk inside. Eventually he relented and came to the gate. He had never heard of Patan but thought there was a market I might find interesting if I continued up the street. It was indeed Patan Durbar Square, my destination.

I navigated a few blocks of construction and winding streets. Suddenly, there like the pot of gold at the end of the rainbow was Patan. It was worth every minute of the walk and the challenges of the open trenches that, when finished, would house water and sewer lines.

Patan was originally designed in the shape of the

Buddhist Dharma-Chakra (Wheel of Righteousness). The four thurs or mounds on the perimeter of Patan are located, one at each corner of the Cardinal compass points. They are known as Ashoka Stupas. Legend has it that when Emperor Ashoka visited his daughter Charumati in Kathmandu he erected five of the stupas, the four surrounding the city and one in the middle. Today there are more than 1,200 Buddhist monuments of various shapes and sizes scattered around the city.

The monument that gets the most attention is the stone at the entrance to Durbar Square which identifies the area as a UNESCO Heritage Site. There are seven individual sites that make up the Kathmandu Valley World Heritage Site.

The arts and culture centre of the country has made the

transition to retail as well. Shops offer much more than the traditional souvenirs, but with the same aggressive sales approach. The market located beside the Heritage stone proved a little more than I could handle. After about an hour I was done with the hawkers following me and telling me that I had promised to buy from them when I first entered the market.

It had been a long day. I admit my patience was not what it needs to be when entering a market like this, particularly if you have already bought more trinkets and prints than you will ever need.

One young lady, who caught my eye when I entered, insisted on selling me an amulet with the all seeing eye of Buddha inlaid in ivory and the Mandala on the back. Her initial offering was 500 rupees for the medallion complete with a chain. I thanked her and politely said that I had enough souvenirs and was out of money. That only fueled the fire because she took my remarks as a bargaining ploy. She stayed with me through the entire visit and kept asking for an offer. She could not understand that I would have gladly paid her the price she was asking if she would stand still long enough for a photo by one of the temples. She did not have time for that. She was too busy pestering me for an offer on what had now become five necklaces. She was going to lose money on the deal, but make it up on volume, just like every other street vendor.

I spent some time speaking to the less aggressive shop keepers about the process of creating prints with hard-carved wood blocks. At least one young lady was more than willing

to show me the process and explain the various figures on the prints. It seemed there was no shortage of deities in Nepalese folklore and more than a few of the figures related to nature and the gods.

I was busy watching women fill their jugs from three fountains at one end of a below-grade pit, when I was approached by a vendor to purchase a silver-headed walking stick. I told him I was not interested and he seemed to get the message. I went back to watching the ordeal of filling jugs with water in the stone-lined pit and carrying them up the stairs.

The stairs provided amusement for the children that had accompanied their mothers on the daily trip to the local water source, but not much else held their interest. The fountains flow continuously, but in the time I watched the three outlets there were at least a half dozen people in line at each waiting for a chance to fill their jugs.

It was not long before I fell prey to another vendor who provided too much character for me to pass. She was standing behind a table of intricately carved items and saw that one carving of an elephant had caught my attention.

"You have a good eye. That is the most beautiful piece I have," she said. "Hand carved from Yak bone." I may have been born at night, but it wasn't last night. I knew the preamble to a high price coming, she did not disappoint me.

"One hundred American dollars." She said. I laughed out loud. She was not hurt but countered with "What do you offer?"

"It is a beautiful piece," I said, "I would go as high as ten for that."

"Ten? You are looking at hand carved bone. I have cheaper ones down here, but not ten dollars for that piece. I will give you a deal because it is the end of the day." There is something magic about a merchant making a sale at any time of the day. If you are the first customer of the day it is important to make a sale because it sets the tone for the day. If it is closing time it is important to have one more sale. If it is midday it is equally critical for some other reason.

I wondered if all Nepalese street merchants go to the same school of classic lines to hook tourists. I was ready for the game and we bartered. I finally succumbed at thirty dollars.

Actually, I thought my pictures of the woman in action were worth that and the bone carving was a bonus. She wrapped it in newspaper and handed it to me. Only then did I realize how heavy synthetic Yak bone is.

As I walked back to the gate, the vendor across the aisle

stopped me, and asked if I needed another one of the same carving.

"How much?" I asked.

"I will match her price," he said with a shake of his head.

"Fifteen bucks?" I said. You will sell me one for 15 bucks.

"It is late in the day and I have not made a sale. How many do you want?" he asked. Now they were selling authentic yak bone carvings at volume discount. I knew I had been taken. I realized my ten dollar opening bid was not that bad.

"Maybe something else? A knife or some other carving." I walked away only to be accosted by the young girl with the medallions. She followed me to my taxi and I thought she was going to get in with me.

I did stop along the way to buy a chess set that fit in a

four inch diameter container. It looked like a coaster set, but contained a full chess set. When opened, the top fit under the bottom to hold the pieces that had been captured and forced through the holes on either side of the playing area. Three dollars is a lot of money, but it was a gift for the young man that is going to become my son-in-law and he does play chess.

The weight of the synthetic yak bone carving made me decide on a cab back to the hotel. The evening was a lot more fun than working on notes. I was only thirty-five dollars lighter for the trip; not bad for the entertainment value alone.

Kumari

Nepal

Hi, I spent the night here in a great hotel, the day after the worst hotel on the trip. Fire codes are a wonderful thing and I will never complain about regulations after some of the locks on the rooms I have been in. This was scary, and at supposedly the best hotels Les.

Home
Box 1607
Altona Manitoba
R0G 0B0
Canada
North America

A9 - The panoramic range as seen from Pokhara Lake 820m.

© Himalayan MapHouse (P) Ltd. GPO Box 3924, Kathmandu, Nepal • Photo: Jagadish Tiwari

Two year old coffee plants are still two years from harvest
but a good investment

Chapter 16
Harie

Harie has made a commitment to the coffee industry in Nepal. He sees it as one of the bright spots in the country's agriculture and is going to be a part of it in every aspect.

Harie began growing the crop and saw the opportunity to develop a small nursery for coffee plants, which he sells to local farmers.

"I started with the nursery to produce plants for myself," he says, "but soon I realized that other farmers needed plants and no one else was growing them. Our first concern is to grow the seedlings for ourselves, but we will sell the extra."

He was one of the first to get involved with the formation of the District Coffee Producers Association which helps with marketing efforts and provides agronomic information about the crop, which is relatively new to Nepal.

Harie wanted to move up the value chain and get more of the final price of the coffee. Instead of selling the raw product, called red cherries, he purchased a small dehuller that strips the outside coating off the beans and increases the value of the crop. He soon realized that he had more capacity than he needed for his own crop and he now buys red cherries from other farmers. He will also toll mill their crop for them before it is sold to the international buyers.

He now has 1,800 plants that have been in the ground

for several years. He has already taken off his first crop. The nursery boasts another 1,800 plants which will be ready to go to the field next year.

Coffee seedlings spend a year to 18 months in poly bags under the protection of a shade roof while they grow to the proper size and strength to withstand field conditions.

He has also found a market for his own ground coffee at the roadside shop he and his brother operate. He sells the coffee in one kilo bags that his daughter packages and seals. Of course he can provide a cup of Nepal's best for you while you wait for the bus to come by.

Harie sees the potential of the coffee business in Nepal, but is faced with the traditional chicken and egg scenario of agriculture producers in a growing market.

"Last year one of the companies, Highland, wanted to buy coffee from Nepal but they wanted 60 tons to meet their demand," he said. "We could only supply 15 tons. That sent them to other suppliers."

Some of Nepal's coffee has found its way to American and Japanese cups with great approval.

Harie wants to capitalize on the image of Nepal and its mountainous regions, producing some of the best coffee in the world. He would like to see it become to the coffee industry what Darjeeling is to tea.

"The industry is too fragmented and spread throughout the country," he said. "We need to have a concentration in the industry so that when international buyers come to Nepal we can meet their demands."

He says that government support is lacking for the developing industry and in many cases people would sooner have land put back into Community Forestry than grow coffee.

Coffee is not an acceptable crop under the Community Forestry program.

"In many cases, coffee is produced in remote areas," he says. "Farmers close to the roads or towns can make more money growing vegetables and selling them locally. They cannot afford to plant a coffee orchard and wait three years before they have a crop to sell."

He said information about the agronomics of the crop is also a drawback. "Farmers do not know how to grow the crop and they are hesitant to make the change to growing it. They are familiar with growing vegetables and so they stay with what they know even if they could make more money with coffee."

Coffee is the latest addition to his farm. He already grows bananas, pears, citrus fruits and vegetables for the markets in Kathmandu.

"Coffee is such a good fit. The high citrus trees provide

the shade it needs, and the vegetables are grown lower," he says. "So we have three crops growing on the same land and helping each other."

The intercropping is not only a good agronomic practice, it also allows for the most efficient use of the narrow terraces that Harie farms. The steep hills on either side of the narrow valley provide great views, but a limited area of arable land.

He says that coffee is already the biggest money maker on his farm, and has tremendous potential for growth.

"A larger industry with more producers will help us," he says. "It will give us the volume of coffee needed to be noticed in the international market."

There are currently two companies, Himalaya Coffee

Company and the Highland Coffee Company that are bidding on his crops. He says that more product would make Nepal a serious contender in the high value coffee trade.

Hello
Spent a day in Kathmandu between paper work and interviews. Taxis are amazing - crowding the city but never there when you need one. Starting to pack up and have more stuff than will fit my suitcase.

Home
Box 1607 Altona
Manitoba Canada
R0G 0B0

Drip irrigation units mean more crop sooner

I t is less plastic than a North American farmer disposes of after mixing a single tank of spray herbicide. By comparison, it is probably less plastic than a North American family puts in their garbage in a week even if they are deliberate recyclers. To a Nepalese farmer it is a life changing piece of equipment.

"It" is a drip irrigation system that consists of a 20 litre container with two spigots that control the flow of water to pipes going across the end of the plot of vegetables. There are t-connectors every 40 centimeters to pipes running down the rows, and holes that allow the water to pass from the pipe to the plants.

"It has changed my life," said Bhudan. "We not only get an extra crop, but I get my vegetables to market earlier when the price is the highest. There are two things that affect the price of vegetables, quality and being the first to market. The irrigation has made all the difference in the world."

The difference between irrigated and non-irrigated plants in the plot of bitter melons could not be more obvious or more dramatic. The plants at the head of the rows that have not received water have a few leaves 12 inches from the ground. The plants in the rows served by the tiny plastic pipes, already have fruit waiting to be picked.

"That is the difference," he says offering me a melon he

has just picked with one hand while pointing at the low bush like plants where we are standing.

The irrigation units start at 1,100 rupees for the smallest one that will serve a plot of 120 square meters. A larger unit will serve 150 square meters and costs about 1,600 rupees.

In the past 18 months IDE has sold more than 1,000 of the units. They also provide information about growing more than one crop per year. The region typically had land lying idle during the dry season, now they are able to produce high value vegetable crops.

Bhudan is a modern farmer by Nepalese standards, and has been an innovator all of his career.

His farm has been equipped with a biogas collector for five years. The manure from his two cows generates enough power for lights and cooking in the family home.

"It is better in summer when it is hot," he says, "not so good in winter when it is cold, but we have enough power for the house." The day that I visited him, the temperatures were touching 40 C. I am sure that there would have been more than enough activity in the pit to generate power for the home.

His hectare-and-a-half of farm land is all terraced. He

produces chilies in the summer, cauliflower and cabbage in the winter, bitter gourds and beans in the spring and throughout the summer he raises tomatoes.

"We grow the local variety of tomato that is not supplied by other parts of the country," he says. "The demand is higher and the price is better for our tomatoes because they are better for chutney. The salad tomatoes are not in as much demand so the price is not as good."

Tomatoes are the only vegetable crop he produces from open pollinated seed. He utilizes hybrid seed for the rest of his production.

"The yield is better and the time to maturity is generally about half of what it is with the open pollinated varieties," he says. "With the hybrids I can have cucumbers to market in 40 days, where the old varieties take 70 days to maturity."

He also grows potatoes, one of the highest value crops produced in the area. He sells them through a local collection center which sells to buyers from Kathmandu. His village is close enough to the city that buyers come to purchase his produce for sale in the city markets.

He has evaluated coffee production for his farm but has decided against it.

"Most of my fields are on the south-facing side of the mountain," he says. "Coffee needs shade. The bright sunlight on the south side does not work well with coffee so I have decided against it."

He knows that it would be a good revenue-generating crop.

"It is good for the farmers on the other side of the mountain who have the north face," he says. "I have to concentrate on crops that can use the sunlight and will get ready for market soon. I have to use the advantage that I have here" says Bhudan.

Maize is one of the crops that utilizes the extra sunlight well. He grows maize and rice for sale. He uses the straw for his livestock which ultimately becomes the power for his house.

"There is more value to the cereal crops than just the seed," he says with a smile, pointing at the pit below his cow pen.

For Bhudan, water is the major challenge on the steep hillsides that he farms. From June to January he has to manage water and drain it from his fields while preventing soil erosion on the steep hillsides. Then, when the weather turns dry, his farm is water- deficient from January to June before nature's tap turns on again.

It is the dry season that has changed with the use of the drip irrigation system. Previously, the land did not produce a crop during this time. Now he grows a vegetable crop that goes to the local market and his income has increased dramatically.

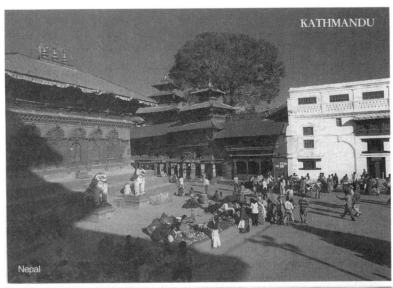

KATHMANDU

Nepal

Hi
Went out to see some drip irrigation - amazing something so simple can make such a difference. Really just a pail and some hose but the veggies are a month earlier

Box 1697
Altona Manitoba
R0G 0B0
Canada
North America

Jeevan Dhungel is the Consular Officer at the Canadian
Embassy in Nepal and a lifeline at times

Chapter 18
CCO Visa

I was ready to spend the day on documentation. I had dropped off the paperwork the night before and all I had to do was pick up my passport, head over to the visa office to get it stamped and all would be well. I planned nothing else for the day, though I knew these tasks should not take more than an hour.

I was headed out of the hotel to catch a cab when I realized I did not have the address of the Canadian Cooperative Office. A phone call to Surendra fixed that. I headed to the parking lot and jumped into the always waiting taxi. I didn't bother negotiating because at this point I was not going to spend 4 minutes to save three dollars. I gave the driver the address, and he headed off the parking lot without any indication that he knew of the street, but we were on our way.

After a few blocks he asked where I was from.

"Canada," I said.

"Oh, that address is the Canadian Cooperative Organization," he said. "Now I know where we are going. Why did you not say CCO?"

Silly me. I thought we needed a street address.

He was a little surprised when I asked him to stop a block earlier, but I explained that I needed to get my passport photos. My man on passport-trature was true to his word and had four pictures waiting for me; four that I trusted were the right size. I gave him the two bucks he requested and waited impatiently as he signed and wrapped each one in tissue paper after blowing the ink dry. He had not quite placed them in the envelope when I grabbed them and ran off to the CCO.

The cabbie said he would wait. I was glad for that knowing that I would only be a couple of minutes. I turned down the lane to the armed guard at the gate, identified myself and was allowed entry.

Over to the office and a request for Jeevan.

He showed up in a couple of minutes and invited me to have a seat. He explained why the process would take an hour. Now that he had all the pieces he could start the process. No pictures, no go. Now we were ready. He assured me I would have everything in an hour. I decided to release my taxi and went out to pay him before settling onto the couch to wait. I had my notebook with me and began to scribble some notes, as much to keep me busy and pass the time as for their value as notes.

Jeevan was a man of his word and returned in about an hour with my emergency passport. He explained its value and that I would have to turn it in when I arrived in Vancouver. I agreed.

With the single page that was now my Canadian passport, and the single most important document I owned, safely in my shoulder bag, I headed out of the CCO with the intention of catching a cab to the building where I was to get the finishing touches – a Nepalese Visa. I was armed with photocopies and originals of the documents I needed for the all-important stamp, plus I had the thirty American dollars that was required for the visa as well. Just in case I had to pay for the re-issuing, I was ready with a ten and a twenty and an extra twenty for the possibility that there was an express line, or some way of speeding the service.

The city was alive with cabs at any time except when I needed one. Here I was waiting to get the documentation that would allow me the trip home and I could not wave down a

Each figure is said to be ten times stronger than the one below it at this stair case

Piggy banks at the potters corner in Bhaktapur

Traditional and western clothing find a comfortable mix

The strong Hindu influence means that cows are sacred and have the right of way.

Vehicles are revered and many carry decorations

A woman carries home feed for her livestock

Coffee loves shade and finds a place on the north face of hills

The steps of the Nyatapola Temple are guarded by mythical beasts

cab in a city that normally had so many taxis on the street it was unsafe to walk.

Finally two stopped, one on each side of the street. The one on the opposite side of the street had stopped a millisecond sooner and I was going to try and get to him when someone on the sidewalk offered advice that may have saved my life. "Take this one," he said, pointing to the one almost on my toes. "It doesn't matter." I jumped in and asked if he knew the building that issued visas. We raced off into the midday heat.

We arrived at the appointed building and of course it wasn't the right building. The one I needed was around back. Some more directions got me to the third floor. That was the visa replacement department, which told me this was a common occurrence. I didn't like the sound of that, but at least I was comfortable with them having a process in place.

I stood at the counter for a while before some bored-looking Government Employee came over and listened to my story. He seemed to understand, but did nothing in response to my situation.

"Can you stamp my passport with a visa?"

"Of course, but we need to know that you had a visa," he said, "then we will stamp it and you are on your way."

I glanced at my watch and calculated that there were 4

hours until Friday afternoon quitting time. That was scary. Very scary.

"We need to check with the airport to see if it was issued," he said. I gave him the date of my arrival and more information that I thought might help. I asked about the express line, pulling the extra 20 from my wallet.

"No," he said shaking his head, "they must check at the airport and if you arrived they will have it. What was the date?"

I wanted to say, "the same as five minutes ago, but thought the better of it and showed him my documentation again.

"It will be ready at 1 o'clock," he said and turned to walk away.

"Are you sure?" I questioned as though it would help. He said it would be ready and moved over to help a young couple that was in need of an extension of their visa or some trivial matter.

I listened to them scream obscenities at the man for a while, in what I decided was a British accent. I wanted to tell them that I found American cash much more effective around the world than loud cursing, but decided that they would learn the lesson themselves soon enough. I have learned that in any country, the lower on the food chain the uniformed attendant is, the more respect he wants.

The lowest guy needs to be treated as though he is the President's advisor and then things happen. When people move up the food chain, they demand less respect and you can almost deal with them as an equal when they are actually in charge of something. This guy needed respect, and the kids had not figured that out. Respect and cash are two things you should never leave behind when packing for a trip to a foreign country, especially one with lots of uniformed employees.

I thought it best I not get involved and headed down to the waiting cab. Not paying for the first trip assures you that he will indeed wait for you. I had three hours and I might as well use them more wisely than sitting at a Government building being annoyed by the inaction of a Friday afternoon.

"Can we go to Bhaktapur and be back by one." I asked the cash-hungry driver.

"Sure," he said, "get in." He would have told me we could go to Mars in that time with a side trip to the moon. I fell for it and got in.

We wound our way to the third city that now makes up

Kathmandu and I set out on my whirlwind tour, knowing I had to be back at the car by 12:30 to make the downtown destination by 1:00.

I arrived back at the car by 12:28, ready to go. The streets to downtown had become parking lots and traffic was not moving at all. My stomach dropped as the hands on my watch pointed at 12 and 1. We were not half the distance to downtown.

"The traffic is bad," he said before I could ask. "I did not expect this."

"When does the government office close?" I asked, panic setting in. I thought about the value of a cell phone at this time, but I didn't have one so it was just a fantasy.

"Two o'clock," he said. "Can we be there by then?" I asked, my panic rising to a higher level.

"Of course. We will be there," he assured me. "They are open until two, and we will be there." We pulled in with 15 minutes to spare. I raced upstairs to find the man of little power gone. It was time to panic. I walked through to the office in the back and sat down in front of the desk of the guy not wearing a uniform, obviously the most powerful.

I explained my situation as concisely as possible and asked for the documentation I needed.

"We are checking at the airport," he said. "When did you arrive?"

We were at square one and it was almost closing time. I hit panic mode and decided this guy would not leave my sight until I got the needed stamp. If that meant going to the washroom, so be it. I was his shadow.

He sensed my concern and assured me he would not leave for the day without my passport getting stamped. That scared me and I was checking for a back door that might allow him to pull an impression of Houdini. He was not leaving my sight.

We went through the date thing a few more times and as it neared two o'clock I realized this might be to my advantage. Somehow at five to two they found my name in the big book at the airport; no computer data base here. Stamp, and another stamp and I was done, except for the payment.

That was done upstairs and cost two dollars. I headed up the stairs expecting to see someone locking a cash box. I was not disappointed. The man behind the desk was getting ready to leave on a Friday afternoon and he did nothing to  hide his displeasure at having a customer darken his doorway. The idea that government employees actually work for the citizens of a country is not a common concept. It was an idea that Surendra had taken to heart and often wondered at, but we agreed it was a problem through much of the world.

He did open up the cash box to take the equivalent of two dollars, but of course he had no change. I said that was fine and headed back down the stairs, not too worried about the 50 cents I was sure he had already pocketed.

The little guy without a uniform stamped my page one more time, and I headed downstairs. On the way I could not help but notice three people sitting on a bench outside one of the offices. The same people had been sitting there during my first visit in the morning and during my return. They did not have the look of people who were getting much accomplished. Actually, they had the look of people who would be in the same seats on Monday morning.

My paperwork was complete and I still had time for an interview at Wild Earth.

Mt. Machhapuchhre – Fish Tail

There is frustration and there are really good people! I had some challenge but the fellow at the Canadian Consulate is a life saver. I will be home

Les.

Box 1607
Altona Manitoba
R0G 0B0
Canada
North America

Electricity helps nature in threshing rice

Chapter 19
Bhaktapur

Chuck at breakfast said that Bhaktapur was a must see so I tried to squeeze it in. I should have known better than to try and visit another city in a three hour time block, when something like my visa hung in the balance. I liked Chuck, maybe because he was Canadian, or maybe because we shared the same view of the guy that pretended to be cleaning the swimming pool while we had our breakfast. I trusted his recommendation and I was glad I did.

Chuck was one of the other early risers at the Greenwich Village hotel. We shared a table and stories on more than one occasion. Usually our stories were of what we had done the day before and what we had planned for the day that was just beginning.

A Canadian who moved down to Pittsburgh because of his business interests, he was in Nepal to sign a deal with a computer programming company. He chose Nepal over a couple of other countries — Russia and India — because he found the people easier to deal with. He liked the fact that they actually listened to what the customer wanted rather than telling him what he needed.

Through the course of our morning conversations it was difficult to tell whether he was in the energy business and trying to find a program that would save companies energy or if he was in the information business and trying to supply a program that would save companies money on their energy costs. It didn't really matter. He was here to sign a deal with a computer program writing company for a program that would help companies to better manage their energy costs. It would allow them to keep a more accurate record of the costs in each area of a plant, and also record the efficiency of that area.

He had made the trek to Bhaktapur the first Sunday that he was in Nepal and recommended it. I had spent that first weekend at the dance festival, conducting interviews in the country, and visiting with a lady who produced 200 broilers a turn and was trying to increase the number of birds she got from the hatchery. Chuck meanwhile had been at the UNESCO world heritage site of Bhaktapur and told me about the "living museum".

It is truly that, a living museum. It is not a museum staffed by college students who are filling their summers wearing period costumes and pretending to be in character during their working hours.

Bhaktapur's skyline of ancient temple roofs set against the Himalayan white-capped mountains, is perhaps the most striking part of the city. After that approaching view, everything else seems almost anticlimactic.

It is a city, still as it was centuries ago. I was amazed to see rice being threshed on stones and thrown up in the air to separate the chaff from the kernels. The harvest process had made some concessions to modern technology, however. A fan powered by an electric motor provided the wind for separation of the crop and the chaff.

The city was a strange link between past and modern technology. The 14 kilometers that separated it from Kathmandu at one time, have now been filled in with industrial shops and refugee camps, or more technically correct, camps for internally displaced persons. These people have not been forced to leave their country so they are not refugees by the world's definition, but rather internally displaced persons. As we drove by the acres of tents constructed from blue plastic tarpaulins, I had trouble understanding the difference between being forced from your home in another country, and experiencing a similar fate in your own country, but officially there is a difference.

The inhabitants of Bhaktapur themselves offered the same kind of fascinating contrast, using the techniques of the past and then capitalizing on the situation when tourists stopped to look. I watched an elderly woman spinning for awhile and took a few pictures. As soon as I put my camera down, her hand came up asking for the model's fee. I pretended I did not understand and walked away. Cruel? Perhaps, but if I paid everyone the modeling fee they expected, this book would be a lot more

expensive than it is. The city was living in the past, but able to move into the present with its charges for tourists.

The admission charge to the city was my first clue. The vendor's story about having a souvenir ticket with a picture on it did little to ease my concern about the seven dollar admission price to what was in reality a city with inhabitants. I told him that we did not charge admission to the town where I lived in Canada. He suggested that we should start. I laughed and went through the gates.

My second step had not yet hit the cobblestones when I was pounced on by a young man who began the story of being a college student and working as a guide. He was just getting to the part about being a history major and studying English when I told him to hold the stories and tell me how much he wanted.

"You can give me what you think it is worth," he said. I told him I had an hour. I wanted to see the city and get some pictures. I wanted the tour at high speed and was not looking to bargain on this one.

"Most people give me seven dollars," he said. I said lets get started. Having a local with me to keep away the merchants would be worth the seven bucks. If he did anything as a guide it would be a bonus. He was worth his money several times over.

Bhaktapur has preserved its tradition much more than Kathmandu or Patan, perhaps because of its location and trait of being more self contained. Farmers still provide the city with its food from local fields, and the craftsmen supply every manner of need for household and farm.

The city square is known for its potter's corner which features endless arrays of pots identical to each other. It is overwhelming to see a thousand pots, all supposedly made by hand, but identical to the other 900 plus around it. Part of the attraction of the city is the merchants laying out their wares every morning and collecting them all again that evening and storing them for display the next day, when the entire process is repeated.

I had made it clear to my young guide that I was on a tight schedule and did not want to spend any time with the souvenir hawkers, even if it meant that he had to give up his commission. I would rather see the city and give him a few bucks extra for the time he spent. He nodded that he understood and we headed off to a gallery featuring the Mandalas.

I was like raw meat in a shark tank in that shop. It was early in the day and no other tourists had been by. The proprietor took the time to give me an overview of the process of painting the intricate patterns on the huge paintings, and I spent more than a few minutes watching two young ladies working on huge paintings on the shop wall.

Suddenly I was engaged in a discussion about the safety of wrapping up my purchase and how he would send it home.

I backed up a step or two and looked at the displays of the mandalas (paintings) he had spread on the counter. Prices varied greatly depending on the detail of the painting and the artist. One created by a student was less expensive than one done by a master and there was a mid-range price for the work of students touched up by masters.

It was from this shop that the back cover of the book you are holding was secured. I did not spend a lot of time on copyright procurement because I own the original oil painting.

The price was certainly high enough to include copyright.

Having made at least one purchase and my young guide sure of a kickback, we moved on to the sights of the city.

The crown jewel is the 55 window palace which now houses the country's National Art Gallery. The palace is a creation of terra cotta and wood columns that defy construction methods of modern times. Considering the time of their erection, they are even more of a marvel. The palace was one of the benefactors of the German restoration program of 1974-86, when much of the city was restored with German funding. Prior to that time the city was still showing the effects of a massive earthquake in 1934 that damaged many of the structures. One of the bell towers bears the name of Chancellor Helmut Kohl, the German leader of the day.

Another bell in the other corner of the square carries a more functional name. The Big Bell marks a corner of Big Bell Square and lives up to its name on all counts.

Our final stop was at the N y a t a p o l a Mandir, (Nyata is Nepalese for five) which is the tallest of the city temples at more than 30 meters. It is set upon five square plinths (layers), each square smaller than the one below it. The plinths each feature a two meter statue guarding the temple and each is believed to be ten times

stronger than the one below it. The Malla wrestlers are thought to be ten times stronger than ordinary people. The elephants above them are ten times stronger than the wrestlers. The lions are ten fold stronger than elephants as are the gryphons relative to the lions. The top step holds the goddesses Baghini and

Singhini who are the final guardians.

Bhaktapur was the capital of the valley during the Malla Kingdom of the 12-15th centuries. The Kingdom is still present through architecture as well as legend.

Time may stand still in Bhaktapur, but not for someone who needs a visa and faces an office closing time. It was time to move on. My young guide knew his business well and when

I asked for the price, he smiled and said, "pay what you think it was worth, that is fine."

I knew he was hoping for more. I gave him the seven bucks he quoted at the outset and headed off to my waiting cab.

I could not resist. I had to stop at one more shop. It had an assortment of horns and carved soldiers on the front steps. Inside the proprietor explained that the horn was a traditional instrument used to call the people of a village together. It was not as much a musical instrument as an alarm system. He shared with me the sounds that were possible under the proper operation. I had to admit they certainly did not need amplification of any sort. The volume emitted would either summon people to the village or have them running away in fear of the terrible monster that was invading.

Over the past couple of days I had seen the horns in use at wedding ceremonies throughout the countryside. I assume they are Nepal's equivalent of the Alpine horns of the Swiss Alps and about as easy to transport.

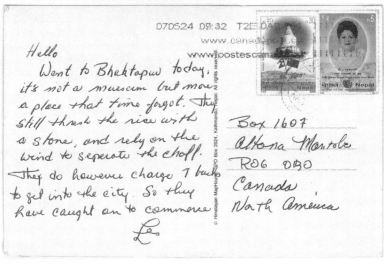

070524 09:32 T2E

www.canada...
www.postescan...

Hello
    Went to Bhaktapur today, it's not a museum but more a place that time forgot. They still thrash the rice with a stone, and rely on the wind to seperate the chaff. They do however charge 1 buck to get into the city. So they have caught on to commerce

Les

Box 1607
Altona Manitoba
R0G 0B0
Canada
North America

Each bar of soap is trimmed by hand at Wild Earth

Therefolks at IDE had suggested that I make a visit to Wild Earth on my first visit to their office and they had not steered me wrong on any of the stories they suggested.

Time was running short, and I had to get my visa. The visit to Bhaktapur had taken much longer than expected because of the traffic and I did not have directions to the Wild Earth facility. When I called to make an appointment for an interview, the lady on the phone suggested that I have my driver call her at the time we were coming and she would provide directions to the shop. That scared me a little, especially after the traffic jam I had just gone through. I thought about canceling and decided not to waste too much time deciding. I headed down to my cab and got going to Wild Earth.

I asked the driver if he had ever heard of it. With the worldwide cab driver look that tells you nothing, he asked if I had a phone number. I gave him the number. He called, and after a few words of English he switched to Nepalese. He talked rapidly for a while and put down his cell phone.

"It is exactly where I thought," he said. "We can be there in ten minutes. They are waiting for you." The situation was so ridiculous I had to laugh out loud. Did he really think that I fell for that line? He had no idea where the place was until he made that phone call. He had gotten the directions and was now ready to get me close to where I was going.

"Let's go, time's wasting," I replied and we raced off the parking lot to be caught in the herd of turtles that is Kathmandu traffic on a Friday, or any other afternoon. We wound our way through a maze of streets that would be alleys in North America. The route we took would be great for a scavenger hunt or some test of how people follow directions. Surprisingly, he deposited me at the gate of Wild Earth before the buildings in the area began to look familiar. I know that a cabbie is lost when buildings start to look familiar. That is a sure sign that we are circling an area. It is usually accompanied by the line, "we are close, and it will only be a couple more minutes."

Carroll Dunham, the founder of Wild Earth, was in a meeting and unable to speak to me. I could understand that her schedule might be full, after me being two hours late for the originally scheduled appointment.

Dunham came to Nepal as an anthropologist to study the practice of fraternal polyandry, where a woman marries all the brothers in a family. After spending several years studying the practice, she fell in love with the country and the villages she stayed in. When she asked the women what she could do to thank them for their hospitality, they replied that some way for them to earn an income would be the greatest help in their lives. Dunham took the request to heart and eventually founded Wild Earth, a company that is committed to generating income for women.

Wild Earth products are based on herbs that are gathered sustainably from community-owned forests and private farms.

The company's mission states: "Nepal is statistically one of the world's most impoverished nations. Wild Earth believes Nepal has rich resources in its herbal tradition and in the diversity of plants that thrive here. We believe that if properly managed, Nepal's rich herbal heritage can sustain rural development."

Today, Dunham is more concerned about providing an income for the women of the country than marriage practices.

Anthropologists cite the harsh climate of the mountainous regions as the reason for the development of the practice of fraternal polyandry. Land is scarce and herding is difficult. The marriage of several sons to one woman meant that less land was required for subsequent generations.

It also meant that in a climate with short life expectancies, a woman and her family would be provided for if she was widowed at a young age. The children of the marriage are treated equally by all fathers, and the mother is the final judge if there is a question as to the biological father of a child.

I spent a few minutes in the gift shop looking at the items

for sale before Deborah Koehler appeared and asked if I would like to go upstairs and see the factory before we sat down to talk about the things they did at Wild Earth. It was an interesting climb up a spiraling metal staircase on the outside of the building. The staircase provided an excellent view of the path that led from the street to the Wild Earth building. I could see into the backyard pen of one of the houses I had passed. My view from this vantage point confirmed that there were indeed cows and goats in the pen and they seemed very much at ease with each other and with the traffic of the city.

A tour of the factory revealed an interesting mix of what could be considered a large test kitchen by North American standards, and rows of soaps drying in wooden boxes. Deborah showed me some soap the company was making for an importing customer. The customer's name was stamped on the soap.

In another area, a half-dozen women sat trimming the edges off the individual bars of soap while in the back of the room a lone male sat at a packaging machine, sealing the bars in their wrapping material. "He is the accountant and one of the few men on staff," she said. "We have about 40 women that work in the shop here. We don't know how many others benefit from the purchase of herbs in the country."

In another room, a woman was preparing sample boxes of the herbs the company uses in production.

The wooden box was about 12 x 6 and contained a grid that made 18 separate compartments. Each compartment would contain a separate herb and a glass cover would be applied before it was shipped to customers in India.

"It's a sample box to show our customers the herbs we use and the different fragrances available," said Deborah.

We were joined by a young woman with a decidedly British accent, who introduced herself as Sam. Sam is the Marketing Manager of Wild Earth and grew up in Cardiff, Wales. Somehow she found her way to Nepal. She bought into the ideology of the company and had the ability to bring her international marketing

expertise and her experience of Nepal together in a product that would touch the lifestyle of the modern consumer.

"It's a walk in the woods," said Sam. "It's the feeling of the woods after the rain, but it is more than that. It is the calm you feel while hiking in the mountains, and it is the feeling of being in the woods after a rain. We want it to be an experience."

I took another sip of my tea. In the company of these two ladies, who I am sure had a million other things to do on Friday afternoon, I took a moment to think about what I had experienced in the last two weeks. Yes there was the traffic and the pollution, but so much more.

My first meeting with the people from IDE had alerted me to the efforts being made to market the products from Nepal. These efforts capitalized on presenting the image of the country to a world that is looking for adventure and nature, all in a safe way. A little splash of adventure to start the day, even if the day will be spent in an office on mundane tasks.

The people at IDE had told me about it. They had showed me some successes and some areas where there were still miles to go before we sleep. They had not steered me wrong on a single lead, and as I conducted one of my last interviews of the trip, I thought how we had come full circle. My stay had concluded with a success story of someone who is truly marketing the mountain.

The methods of this country seemed at odds with each other, just like the technology. I had seen everything from cell phones and spades. Here was the same thing. We were in a factory that employed women to cut every bar of soap by hand, and we were talking about marketing efforts world wide. Sam could reach people on the world wide web, but she was concerned about portraying the right image of the

company and providing products people wanted.

Deborah spoke about the demand for products in India and China and the wealth of these emerging countries.

"The demand from these countries is more than we can keep up with," she said. "They have emerging wealthy classes. By the sheer numbers of their populations, they are large markets."

I could not help but think that we are on the outside looking in. The products that Wild Earth is developing are not targeted at North American markets, but rather at the huge markets of India and China right next door. We remain stuck in our thinking of the past, that China and India are developing countries. They may well be still developing, but they have developed an affluence that has surpassed North America. Much of the world already understands that.

I came back to reality and asked Sam about the future of Wild Earth marketing.

"We have some new products that are coming along," she said. "New product development is different here because we rely on the methods of the past, not on developing a fragrance in the lab. There is so much potential as the world becomes more aware of some of the natural powers of plants."

It was time to head off to my waiting taxi. I had told him that I would be an hour and it was now well past two hours. I had no fear that he would have left, since I had not paid him for any of the day's fares. He showed no displeasure when I arrived, asking only for the next stop.

I told him the day was over and it was time to get back to the hotel. He asked if I would need a car later or perhaps tomorrow. I assured him I was done.

We pulled into the hotel and I asked him about the fare. He smiled and said it had been a long day and that I could decide.

I handed him 2,000 rupees knowing it would be more than a month's wages for many people in the city, but I have always said that a good wheel man is worth a lot of money. This guy was a dandy. Sure he had pulled a few of the traditional cabby tricks with directions, but he got me everywhere I wanted to go and in good time. I had no regrets about giving him a few extra bucks. He had helped me do my job.

The Dudh Koshi Trail

Hi

There are some companies that are taking this image to the world. I visited a "Body Shop" kind of place that has a huge market - Dudie

Box 1607
Altona Manitoba
R0G 0B0
Canada
North America

Hotel Greenwich had been my home for two weeks

Chapter 21
Saturday

T hings were winding down., I had one more day before I left and I wanted to make sure that I used it to the greatest benefit. That meant an early start and getting out to see more of the city.

When I went downstairs to have breakfast, I was more than a little surprised to see Bikram Lama (Rob) waiting for me in the lobby.

Rob was the taxi driver's brother from my first excursion to Tamil. He had offered to arrange an airplane tour of the mountains for me for that morning, but I had decided against it. It was not that I didn't trust him, it was just that very few people are listed as Trekking Guides and Social Workers on the same card. I did not see how the two could be related. I could see how a tour to a mountain village could bring about some extra income for the village and that might be considered a social service, but I remained cautious and chose not to book an airplane flight with him.

He had also offered to look after my flight home. Even though it was Saturday, he claimed to have the cell phone number of the office manager at Thai Airlines. He would contact him and make sure that I was booked aboard the flight on Sunday.

Rob was not charging me for his services so I agreed.

He made a call and returned in a few minutes telling me that all was looked after.

I asked him how he could do that on a Saturday when everyone else said the office was closed. He explained that his cousin cleaned the offices of Thai Air and therefore had contact with the manager. He had gone through his cousin to confirm my reservation (the next two chapters explain how well that went).

He assured me the travel arrangements had been looked after and was ready to provide me with interesting tours for the rest of the day. I excused myself several times and told him that I would be just fine. He could not accept me being on my own on my last day in Nepal and wanted to do something he could charge me for, or he could get a commission for.

I agreed to meet him in Tamil at 4 o'clock that afternoon. I had a few things I needed to do and this was the only way that I could get him to leave.

I headed poolside to my usual spot for breakfast, and as usual it was not ready. I helped myself to a coffee and sat down thinking about how much I missed a Saturday morning paper. As if on cue a fellow came through the lobby with the local papers, and after dropping some off in the lobby, delivered one to my table. Things were getting better. With the paper to hold my attention, I was able to wait for breakfast.

The paper carried the same stories as it had all week about the problems in parliament with eight parties all trying to have their say. Of course the Prime Minister was saying that he could not do anything in a parliament that was split so many ways, and that his government would like to move on the issues of the day but the opposition would not allow him. There was also a story on the fuel crisis and problems at the Indian border. I thought back to my visit there and how the crisis was mostly the Black Marketeers waiting for the price to go higher so they could take more profit from their purchases.

The Communist insurgents had also made another strike and another eight lives had been lost. Breakfast was on the table and that took my attention.

I was enjoying my eggs and thinking there was no oil shortage in the kitchen when Sheri joined me at the table. Sheri was a Project Director of International Development with the Canadian Bar Association and originally from Alberta. She now called Ottawa home when she was in Canada.

During the past week we had met several times over breakfast and discussed the matters of our country and the one we were visiting. One of the days our talk had turned to Quebec. I have had enough experience with Albertans to know their view on that situation, but I found her view interesting.

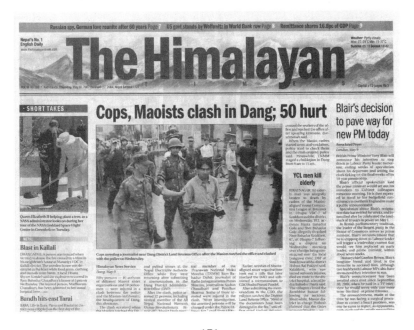

"It may not be a perfect solution," she said, "but to the rest of the world, our dealings with Quebec are enviable." I had not heard this view before, but as I listened to her I had to agree. What we think is a problem in our country would be viewed as a peaceful solution in most parts of the world. There has not been open warfare and the only life lost was in the 1970's. Comparatively, the insurgents had just killed eight people the previous night in this country.

She explained that there was not only development work in rural areas to be done in this country. "The places you visited need help with agriculture," she said. "I am here to help them develop a legal system that deals with the problems of the day. Just as you have seen the tremendous difference between subsistence agriculture and producing for world markets, the same thing exists in their legal system."

It was a point I had not considered. I try to stay away from the legal system whenever possible in Canada. I had not considered that we are leaders in this arena, and we have the opportunity to show leadership in developing legal systems.

Breakfast was done but there was still more coffee and neither of us had any pressing appointments, so we decided to solve a few more of the world's problems.

I asked her about our role or our obligation to other countries with respect to the environment. I was sure an Albertan would have an opinion on this one.

"How do we handle the rest of the world?" I asked. "Do we force our values on developing nations and make their development environmentally sound, even if it comes at great expense?"

Her view was that we (North Americans) had some obligation to provide leadership in developing countries, but we could not do it heavy handedly, especially since our own record was not that good.

I agreed and mentioned what the white man had done to the buffalo in North America. Now we were quite self righteous in protecting endangered species in Africa. She had a few more examples that hit home.

The legal aspect of international development is one I had not even considered and I thanked her for her time and insight. I was glad I had met her.

Machhapuchhre 6997 m.

POKHARA

nepal.

Hi, I'll be home before this card - hope my luggage makes it. I am packing and can not believe the stuff I have bought P.

Box 1607
Altona Manitoba
R0G 0B0
Canada.
North America

I was going home, but what does her future hold?

T he wakeup call came at 5:30, just as I had requested. I think it was the only one on the entire trip that was on time. It didn't matter because I had been up for at least half an hour and had almost finished packing.

I knew that I had been acquiring a lot of goods, but the amount of them and their weight really hit home when I tried to stuff them into my Roots roller bag, and my newly acquired piece of Eastern European luggage. Eastern European luggage is my name for those cheap nylon bags, that are usually some variation of blue and red plaid, and come equipped with two handles that rip off the first time you lift the bag with more than its own weight. It was cheap and it would allow me to get my belongings home, which was all I asked from it, then it would be included in the trash the next Tuesday morning (Tuesday is garbage day on our street).

I tried to wrap my original yak bone carving in a few shirts and place it at the centre of the Roots bag. I surrounded it with pants and my newly acquired garments. (Like the shirt I realized I would never wear in Canada, but that is what travel is about.)

I wondered why I had bought my wife four diffcrent silk scarves. Even though the price per unit had come down with the multiple purchase, I could not see any point in it now.

One last lukewarm shower and it was time to put the final items in the bag and get down to breakfast. I was scheduled to have my last meeting with Surendra and when he arrived at 6:10, the breakfast service was still not open. I knew that they posted opening hours just as a guideline, but I had hoped that maybe just once they could be on time. It didn't happen.

Coffee was ready soon enough and Surendra and I took time for one last visit. His brother had been in a motorcycle accident and was having major repair work done to his leg. I told him I was sure that I could handle the airport trip on my own, even though I knew his offer to accompany me was genuine.

I caught a cab to the airport, assuming that I would need extra time to purchase a ticket and there might be a few challenges. In Nepal, like at home, traffic is not a problem when you are early . It is only when you are late that the streets become parking lots. I got to the airport by 9 and had two porters accost me before I could get my rear and my gear out of the cab. The airport did not open until 10 o'clock, but the airline office in the next building was apparently open, and the older of the pair of porters said he knew where I needed to go.

My luggage guarded by the younger of the two, I followed the older man to the next building, past the armed guard and down a corridor marked No Admittance. The armed fellow was yelling at us. I never like the feeling of a guy with a gun yelling at me, but we carried on up a couple of flights of stairs, down a dark hallway and right to the Air Hong Kong office.

The fellow behind the desk was doing his best to answer some frantic customer's queries in English and waved at me to sit down. After a few minutes of assuring the customer of whatever she wanted, he turned to me. I explained that my tickets and passport had been stolen and I would like to purchase a ticket.

"You can only do that at the office downtown," he said. "Our main office is downtown and they handle the ticket sales. You cannot buy a ticket at the airport." It suddenly became clear to me. This was the same airport where I had not been able to buy an entry visa in the local currency. Why then would they sell tickets here?

The fellow explained that I could check my luggage and then take a cab downtown to buy a ticket. My old friend was waiting at the door, and I followed him past the armed guard and back to our waiting (younger) friend who had been guarding my luggage. He was still there. I gave the old fellow the equivalent of two dollars and headed into the terminal to face another conundrum. How do you get past security without a ticket? Put your head down and walk like you know where you're going. I did.

To my surprise, when I lifted my luggage onto the scale to check in, it was none other than the fellow from upstairs in the other building who was applying the tags. I began to explain the situation.

"Yes, I know," he said. "I will keep your bags here. Go downtown and buy a ticket." I turned and headed to the line of waiting taxis. We were off to the downtown office. We got there just in time for opening at 10.

Suffice it to say that there were a few challenges in purchasing a ticket and applying it to my credit card, but it got done and we were not much the worse for wear. I took a worse beating from the fellow who tried to sell me some carved

elephants as I made my way back to the car. He hit the wrong guy on the wrong day. I had already checked my luggage, and knew that I had more souvenirs than I needed. I was more concerned about me getting home than having a carved elephant or two with me. Things turned ugly and he almost lost a hand in the car door of the taxi. My rule is, after the third "no" leave me alone and don't touch me, especially when I am in the car. Perhaps I am too sensitive on this issue, but that is my rule and offenders are in dangerous territory.

The cab driver saw my reaction and decided not to bother me. He must have read my mind because we headed straight back to the airport.

I had cooled off a little by then; not because of the temperature in the taxi, but because of the slow deep breaths. Lots of them.

I tested the security again, this time with a ticket and no luggage. The line consisted of at least a half-dozen men who must have been leaving the country for the final time. Why else would they be taking all their worldly possessions with them? The fellow behind me was incredibly nearsighted; so much so that he could not see the front of his luggage cart which was hitting the back of my ankle. On the third hit, I turned around and asked him if he would like to go ahead of me for my own safety.

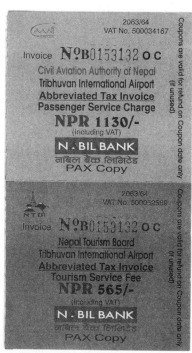

He thanked me and moved to my place in line. It appears that sarcasm is not recognized in Nepal.

Next stop, the departure tax wicket. I had just enough cash for that. I found it strange that they accept any form of currency, including plastic, when you are leaving the country. It must be that a different fellow owns this business than the entry one.

I headed over to the gate and got the luggage tags attached to my ticket. I was feeling much more confident now about this trip. I felt I would be able to get through with my makeshift passport and a working Visa card, (not the kind issued by a government, but the kind from a bank.)

I went upstairs and looked for the gate that I was to leave from. As a final irony, I was too early. The security gates, which looked a lot like two folding tables, were not yet occupied. A lone fellow sat dozing in a chair nearby. He told me they would open an hour before departure time. I had an hour to kill before that happened. There was an internet café across the hall and I thought it might be my last chance to leave a message for home. I spent what amounted to my last 40 cents of change on a half-hour of internet. I did not even use all of it because the proprietor assigned me to a computer next to his and he happened to be a chain smoker. I really didn't want to spend the next two days smelling like an ashtray. I got up to leave after twenty minutes, as though that would really make a difference in the odor that clung to my clothes. Nice try, but I already smelled like Nepalese cigarettes and I was not going to have a chance to change clothes until I got home. I considered it a cultural experience and headed back to the security area to wait for the guards to arrive.

The first check of my documentation went smoothly, but the second check at the next set of doors caused some problems. I was sent back to the original gate to get one more stamp.

Some little fellow with a big stamp made me sit and wait for another ten minutes before he realized that I was at least as stubborn as he was, and I was going to stick with my story no matter how often he asked about it. He relented and gave my paperwork three massive stamps, with all the power he could muster. I went back through gate number one, passed inspection at gate number two as well, and made it to the passenger lounge. My spirits soared.

A Bugs Bunny cartoon was on TV screen in the passenger lounge. Since the Bunny has always been one of my favorites, I settled into watch it and spend my last hour in Nepal. It was the cartoon where Bugs talks to the artist about how he should be drawn. The artist comes back with various bodies, like a

179

donkey and Daffy Duck. I thought about how fitting the cartoon was for this country. Just like a cartoon character telling the artist what kind of body it wants, Nepal's development and movement to the modern world is strangely at odds with the present reality. The country has so many natural resources, yet it is one of the poorest in the world. It has one of the most diverse plant populations, but it is only now beginning to harvest the natural plants and sell them to an ever-growing market. Recipes developed over many generations, are now being used by the wealthy in developed countries. It seems like a Bugs Bunny cartoon that has so many messages at so many levels.

I moved to the massive room that served as a holding area for people waiting to walk out on the tarmac. There I met Chuck, the transplanted Canadian computer guy. There were no less than three flights leaving in the next couple of minutes and the passengers from all three were mixed in the holding area. Organization of air transport is not a priority in Nepal. Chuck headed off to his flight. I turned the other way to mine.

The flight to Bangkok was relatively uneventful after the scruffy-looking backpacker got sitting down. A pack that is proper gear for trekking the Himalayas, adds a new dimension to the bull in a china shop analogy in an airplane. He turned around twice and was well on his way to duplicating the Abbott and Costello skit where they try to go through a doorway with a ladder sideways. The backpacker clipped me in the head twice, but eventually he got sitting down, much to everyone's relief.

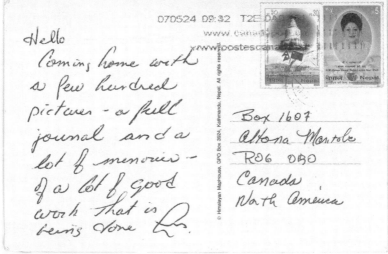

Hello
Coming home with a few hundred pictures - a full journal and a lot of memories - of a lot of good work that is being done

Box 1607
Altona Manitoba
R06 0B0
Canada
North America

Bangkok airport offers a mix of traditional and European cultures

Chapter 23
Bangkok

I t was my third time in the Bangkok airport in the past month and I was beginning to feel like I could handle the challenge. The first time, I had the benefit of a Calgary couple to help me through the army of people trying to get my money. The second time I fell prey to the typical cab driver ruse of knowing where my hotel was until I was on the bridge into town and then the price escalated. But this time I was ready for an adventure and I didn't need a hotel downtown since I would be leaving early the next morning.

I made my way to one of the countless hotel counters and asked about a room. The price seemed reasonable enough, the pictures looked good and the lady behind the counter spoke English that I could understand. What more could I ask for?

I asked for an Air Canada counter. I still needed a ticket from Hong Kong to Winnipeg and the only place I could get one was at an Air Canada office. The young lady told me there was one on the fourth floor, and I could go there as soon as I got the hotel paper work done. I smiled and told her I would do the ticket stuff first and come back to her. She said she would wait.

A trip to the fourth floor yielded no Air Canada office. There was an information desk that confirmed there was no office in Bangkok, but there was one in New Delhi. That didn't help me much and I returned to book a hotel.

The young lady was still waiting at the counter, having sold a few other rooms in the meantime, I am sure. I booked a room for about 50 bucks. It included taxi fare to and from the airport and breakfast. I was not about to argue with that. I was getting tired and wanted to get some sleep because I knew I had two days of travel ahead of me.

She told me that I would be sharing the cab with a couple of other fellows. I had no problem with that and she gathered the three of us and assigned a point for us to wait for the driver. Obviously she had been a kindergarten teacher in her previous life, but we followed orders.

One of the other fellows in the car was originally from Texas. He had attended a Bible School in Nepal and had become very close to the family he stayed with while in school. He had returned for a family wedding and was heading back to California where he was attending school now. The third rider was of the non-talkative variety. He offered no information on his life journey, and we didn't press him.

The taxi driver dropped us off at what looked like an apartment complex and assured us that it was our hotel. We went in and registered in what seemed like a great deal of

uncertainty. We were assigned our rooms and told that the dining room and massage rooms were just down the hallway on the ground floor of the hotel.

I deposited my bag in my room and went down to try to get my email and a bite to eat. What was billed as a business center in the brochure at the airport, was a computer in one corner of the lobby. It provided entertainment for the teenage girl at the desk when she was not registering a guest.

I asked her if I could use the computer. She paused her game and allowed me to sign in and get some mail from home. While I was checking the mail, a couple returned from an obviously all-day excursion and picked up their keys. Soon we were in a discussion about their day. They were exclaiming about the tiger preserve they had been to and how difficult it had been to find.

We agreed to have supper together. They dropped their gear in their rooms, I finished my correspondence and we headed off to the dining room that looked a lot like the lunch room at any small business. It had one of those sliding door Coke coolers in one corner and about four kitchen chrome sets in the rest of the room. A television sat on a shelf in the corner about six feet off the floor. Someone in the next room must have been a motor sports fan, because the volume was so loud that it was painful for anyone in the room. It must have been for the benefit of someone outside the room.

My new friends and I sat down to trade a few stories and enjoy supper.

The woman explained that they were brother and sister. After the breakup of her marriage she traveled with her brother because he was the only one who shared her sense of adventure.

Their story of the trip to the tiger compound was a great one. If there was any doubt, the pictures verified their story. What did we do before digital cameras?

She ordered a bowl of fish curry soup that looked and smelled delicious. I did the same and understood that curry in this place meant spicy. It was a meal in itself and one of the best of the trip. The shrimp were the size of breakfast sausages and the rice was not in a softball-size glump at the bottom of the bowl.

She explained that the hotel was a recent conversion from an apartment block. A family had bought it, converted it to a hotel and was doing all the work in the hotel themselves. That explained some of the uncertainty at check-in time.

She was heading off for a massage and I asked about the price. While it was not quite as cheap as the foot massage I had at the downtown hotel, it was still very reasonable. I decided to spring for the four dollars, for the hour long Thai Massage. The masseuse asked me if I wanted the light or the medium massage. I chose medium just because I didn't know the difference.

A cup of coffee and an hour-long massage had me ready for bed. I returned to my room with little concern about its Spartan décor. It served the function. I was ready to sleep and the room had a bed.

The next thing I knew it was time to get ready for a trip to the airport. The wakeup call came at approximately the right time.

I dined alone that morning. My friend from California was to be on a flight at the same time, but did not appear for breakfast, which consisted of some of the most thinly sliced toast I have ever experienced, a couple of hard fried eggs and two triangles of ham that must have been sliced with a ginsu knife. That's the knife that used to run TV adds saying you can slice tomatoes so thin your relatives will never come back.

The coffee was good, and a great kick start to the day.

A car was waiting and I was off to the airport.

I was starting to get comfortable with the departures from here, and the added benefit of no luggage to check helped the process. I waited at the Thai Airways counter check-in and could not believe it when the lady gave me three boarding passes. She included the boarding pass for Hong Kong to Vancouver, and Vancouver to Winnipeg. That was a part of the journey I did not even have a ticket for, but I was not going to ask her about it. My feeling was, if you have the boarding pass you have a seat. That is all I wanted.

She pointed me to the booth where I had to pay the departure tax. When I returned she gave me the passes and said my luggage had been checked through to Winnipeg. Things were looking up, but I wasn't taking any chances. I made my way to security and faced a few questions about the lack of a passport and the single sheet of paper that was labeled "emergency passport." Finally the young fellow at the gate got tired of the game and let me go through. I wasn't much in the mood for shopping at the duty free shop. I spent the hour I had to spare chatting with a woman from Australia who had just spent a month in India. She was returning home and looking

forward to less aggressive marketing, and warm showers. I told her I understood her feelings.

No problems at the gate and I was on my way to Hong Kong. That was the airport that was going to be the dicey part of my trip. I only had 45 minutes between flights and I was told that I had to go to Air Canada and purchase a ticket for the last two legs of my journey. I was willing to give it a try with only the boarding passes that I had received in Bangkok. I

CANADA

EMERGENCY PASSPORT FOR A
SINGLE JOURNEY ONLY

PASSEPORT PROVISOIRE VALABLE
POUR UN SEUL VOYAGE

No EC017186

PARTICULARS OF BEARER – SIGNALEMENT DU TITULAIRE

Family Name / Nom	KLETKE
Given Names / Prénoms	Leslie Myles William
Date of Birth / Date de naissance	23 July 1955
Place of Birth / Lieu de naissance	Altona, Manitoba, Canada
Colour of Hair / Couleur des cheveux	Brown
Eyes / Yeux	Green
Height / Taille	5'10"
Weight / Poids	224 lbs.
Citizenship status of bearer / Citoyenneté du titulaire	Canadian

PHOTOGRAPH - PHOTOGRAPHIE

Les Kletke

Signature of bearer/Signature du titulaire

PARTICULARS OF PASSPORT – DONNÉES DU PASSEPORT

Issued for a single journey to
Émis pour un seul voyage à destination de _____ **Canada**
Country/Pays

via **Thailand and Hong Kong**   Mode of Transport
Countries/Pays   Moyen de transport **By Air**

Arriving at   **Vancouver**   on   **14 May 2007**
Arrivée à   Port of Entry/Point d'entrée   le   Date

Purpose of trip
But du voyage **To return home**

THIS EMERGENCY PASSPORT EXPIRES ON
CE PASSEPORT PROVISOIRE EXPIRE LE   **21 May 2007**
Date

Issued at
Émis à **Kathmandu, Nepal**   on   **11 May 2007**
le   Date

Consular Officer
Signature of Issuing Officer/Signature de l'agent émetteur   Title/Titre

OBSERVATIONS

FOR FILE
PAX FILE
UK10605

IMPORTANT – See reverse side - Voir au verso

188

have never seen anyone refused with a boarding pass, well perhaps I have, but I was putting that out of my mind.

Flight completed, we landed in Hong Kong and I had time to get to the next gate. Things were working and then the bubble burst. As I handed the attendant my boarding pass at the door to the walkway for my flight to Vancouver, something wasn't right and I got the, "Please step out of the line, and come over here."

I was not giving up. I believe that people are reasonable and if I told my story in a calm and rational manner this could still work. I knew that the "insisting and then yelling route" was not going to work. All they had to do was detain me for five minutes and once the plane left, I was done. So I told the story about having my passport and tickets stolen for what seemed to be well over the hundredth time.

All it got me was a call to another Air Canada employee to come and listen to it again. The rest of the passengers on the flight had now made their way through the door of the terminal and were on their way to the plane. I was approaching zero hour.

"You don't have a ticket," said the latest person to arrive in what was now a small crowd of Air Canada employees.

"Yes, I know. It was stolen," I replied as politely as I could. "I could not buy one in Nepal or Bangkok and since I had a boarding pass I thought I was all right.

"You have to buy a ticket," he said.

"I would like to do that. Can you sell me one?" The question seemed to stump him. He called another employee who could handle that. I thought I heard the pilot rev the engine, but maybe it was just the blood rushing to my head.

Suddenly a credit card machine appeared from under the desk and the last person into the fray filled out the form and rang me up. I signed the document, grabbed my one time passport and headed off down the walkway.

Next stop Vancouver.

I have sometimes been amazed at how difficult it is to get back into your own country, and this would be one of those times.

We landed in Vancouver. I did the mandatory baggage claim and carried my bag to the carousel that would take it to the plane to Winnipeg. It was time to deal with the passport issue. Of course I could not be processed at the regular desk and had to be sent to the area I thought was reserved for criminals and questionable characters.

The officer handling my entry was polite, if not pleasant and stamped my single sheet of paper. I made sure that I was admitted to the country before I asked any questions. I asked if I could have a copy of the document, which she was required to take from me.

I explained that it was only for my files. She had trouble understanding that. I was planning to visit my son in Iowa the next weekend and thought maybe it might help if I ran into a border issue, but there was no point in explaining that to her. She agreed to make a photocopy, but when I asked for both sides, we ran into trouble.

"No, that is not possible." She said.

I tried to explain that I wanted a copy of the back because of all the stamping it had received in Nepal and I would like to show my friends. I didn't mention that I wanted to show it to you, the reader. That would have been big trouble.

"It's for your records only?" she asked again.

"Yes, just for my files," I said.

"One side, that's it." She was firm.

I love this country and the way that our freedoms and

rights are protected. I really do, but sometimes people in uniforms get a little carried away with themselves. I thanked her and found my way to the gate for the Winnipeg flight.

Hello,

Hong Kong airport is quite an experience. It is only a couple of years old and designed to handle people. It is like a free way for air travellers. The shops are designed to have you spend some money to but it is a great place to transfer planes and has an Air Canada office

Home
Box 1607
Altona, Manitoba
Canada
R0G 0B0

Les Kletke is a freelance writer, author, and speaker. His earlier books recount adventures on the Trans Siberian Railway, and a camel and truck trek that took him across Morocco.

In the past two decades he has visited over thirty countries. Always an observer of the human element, his books are more than a collection of facts and figures, they are the stories of his travels and his interaction with the people of the places he visits.

Les holds a degree in Economics and a Diploma in Agriculture from the University of Manitoba. He is also a graduate of the Continental School of Auctioneering.

Marketing the Mountain is Les' 6th book and is part of a two book set commissioned by International Development Enterprises.

You can order his books at www.leskletke.com